UNIVERSITY OF KNOWLEDGE
GLENN FRANK, B.A., M.A., LITT.D., L.H.D., LL.D., *Editor-in-Chief*

PRINTED AND BOUND IN THE UNITED STATES
OF AMERICA BY THE CUNEO PRESS, INC.

Courtesy Geological Survey, U. S. Dept. of Interior

SURVEYORS AT WORK BELOW BOULDER RAPIDS IN MARBLE CANYON

UNIVERSITY OF KNOWLEDGE

GLENN FRANK, EDITOR-IN-CHIEF

THE STORY

OF

ENGINEERING

BY

J. GARDNER BENNETT, B.S., C.E.

*Professor and Head of the
Department of Civil Engineering,
Lewis Institute, Chicago*

AND

ASSOCIATES

o

UNIVERSITY OF KNOWLEDGE, INCORPORATED

CHICAGO

INTRODUCTION

This is a book about the engineer and what he has done to our lives, to our enterprises, and to our civilization. This volume rightly lists the engineer, along with the scientist and the inventor, as among the Men Against Darkness, the men who have brought light and leadership to the lives of their fellows and to the life of the future.

Who is this person called Engineer that he should be listed among the Men Against Darkness?

When I was a lad in Missouri, an engineer meant but one thing to me—the man who ran the engine of the one mail train that went through my incredibly small home village of Greentop each day. Since then I have come to know the engineer in the broader sense of the man who puts science and invention actually at work in the service of man. It is not too much to call the modern engineer the liaison officer between science and society.

There are multiplied thousands of things the engineer has done for us, specific things, machines, processes, arrangements that have made our factories more productive and our homes more livable. All these are told about in this volume. And they are told about with a degree of detail I would not have believed possible in a book that covers as much ground as this book covers. It would be beside the point for me to summarize here the mass of specific things the engineer has done for us. That is all in the body of the book. Any one of these separate things the engineer has done brings a round of applause. But the engineer is not as popular in some quarters as this might suggest. There are those who insist that the engineer has fallen down on his job because the machine age and power age he has ushered in have not brought in the utopia some press agents of the machine and power age had predicted.

What about this indictment of the engineer?

Let us admit at the outset that machines have thrown men out of work and that power production has piled up surpluses that could not readily be sold at a profit. Is this the fault of the engineer? I do not think so. The engineer, in bringing the thought of the scientist and the devices of the inventor into the field of practical operation, has, for the first time in human history, made possible the conquest of the age-old tyrannies of poverty, drudgery, and insecurity. After centuries of scarcity, the engineer has made possible an age of plenty. And yet we are citizens of an age in which a distressing number of our fellows are on a less-than-civilized income and our economic order is cursed with stubborn unemployment and recurrent depressions.

Why? Is the engineer to blame? Yes and no!

The machines that the engineer has set in motion have made more jobs than they have destroyed. The motive power which the engineer has set free has made possible a mass production which, in turn, has made possible higher wages, shorter hours, and lower prices. And yet depressions come and ten million or more workmen walk the streets without jobs and press their claims at the gates of government. This is why I say yes *and* no to the query: Is the engineer to blame?

If we look only at the machines, processes, and arrangements the engineer has set at work, we must say that he is *not* to blame. As the bringer-into-action of the results of research, the engineer has set going the machines, developed and applied the processes, and effected the organized arrangements that have made an age of plenty possible. But our social policies have, it seems, not kept pace with the social changes produced by research and the engineer's application of its results. The development of scientific processes has moved with airplane speed. The development of social policies has lagged at a stagecoach rate. The physical sciences have produced social changes faster than the social sciences have perfected social controls. All sorts of maladjustments have occurred. The result has been a race between scientific progress and social instability, with instability, for the time being, in the lead.

It is absurd to assume that a race intelligent enough to invent and develop the giant forces of physical science, industrial technology, and power production cannot devise and perfect policies that will put the full fruits of these forces into effective human use for the millions.

The engineer has done a magnificent job to date. He cannot be asked to assume the total blame or the fact that all of his results have not been wisely used by society. On the other hand, the engineer can play a larger part than he has in seeing to it that the results of science, technology, and power are used to wider human advantage and in the interests of greater social stability.

What is needed is a closer co-operation between the physical scientists who produce social changes and the social scientists who are supposed to be expert in devising social uses and controls. The engineer is a connecting link between the physical scientists and the social scientists. He has a rare opportunity, in this age of confusion and instability, to say to both something like this:

"As engineer I take the discoveries and inventions that come out of physical science research and apply them to the life and work of the world. I do this in the high hope that these discoveries and inventions will push mankind a bit further toward the conquest of poverty, drudgery, and insecurity. Again and again I am disappointed. I find machines throwing men out of work. I find increased productive efficiency creating surpluses that cannot be sold, with the result that prices collapse and depression blights our common life. When all this happens, the social scientists rush in as a kind of wrecking crew to clean up after the catastrophe and to suggest ways of preventing its recurrence. But this means that the social scientists get into the game too late. I propose, therefore, that in all our universities, research institutes, and industrial laboratories the physical scientists and social scientists work out a method for frequent conference *during* their researches rather than *after* their researches. I want the social scientists kept constantly informed about what the physical scientists are up to, not after the physical scientists have worked social and economic havoc with their discoveries, but from the very beginning of their researches. This is why I think this is important. If the chemists or physicists are on the trail of a new idea in 1938 which may, by 1958, result in a new process that will revolutionize industry and produce all sorts of social and economic readjustments, the social scientists should know it in 1938, not in 1958. And, through all the twenty years from 1938 to 1958, the social scientists should be considering ways and means of making this new process help instead of hamstringing humanity if and when it becomes workable."

If the engineers demanded this, they could get it. And if we could insure some such method of sustained co-operation between the physical scientists and the social scientists, I am convinced that we could shorten by at least a decade the lag between the swiftly changing processes and the slowly changing policies of our national life.

Just because the engineer is the man who applies the revolutionary results of research to our lives and to our work, it is important, if we are to understand our day and generation, that we know something of the story of the impact of engineering upon the life of our time. This is why this volume on engineering is included in this series.

GLENN FRANK, *Editor-in-chief.*

PREFACE

Many centuries ago the deserts of Asia were fertile regions teeming with life. Men found there the means with which to build cities and to support large populations. Climatic changes slowly turned those ancient Edens into oceans of drifting sand that drove the people from their homes and buried their villages. When a party of explorers found the ruins of one of these early communities, the place was revealed by fragments of buildings which survived the ravages of time. Nature had obliterated almost every trace of the inhabitants, but the work of primitive architects remained.

Egypt, Syria, and Babylonia; Troy, Knossus, and Mycenae; Athens, Rome, and Chichen Itzá—all testify to the remarkable skill with which engineering problems were met and solved in past eras. The temple of Amon at Karnak, on the site of ancient Thebes, is remarkable for its massive columns and bold conception. Roman highways and aqueducts, amphitheaters and bridges, excite the wonder of visitors. Engineers in the Incas' service threw swaying suspension bridges across the narrow gorges of the Andes, and built royal pathways along the edges of awful precipices.

There is hardly a field of engineering which has not been enriched by previous civilizations. Architecture, navigation, highway construction, mining, military machines, transportation, city planning, and water systems have attracted the attention of technical experts throughout the ages. Frequently they discovered fundamental principles which could not be applied until science and invention furnished the materials and tools. The famous Hero of Alexander was a mechanical engineer who demonstrated the power of steam centuries before Newcomen and Watt. Wooden rails were used in mines before they were used on the surface. With the achievements of metallurgists and tool makers at hand, railroad builders spanned the continents with narrow steel ribbons.

Modern civilization, in its technical aspects, is a monument to the resourcefulness of the engineer. From his blueprints and plans come massive buildings and cozy bungalows. He burrows into the earth for precious metals and taps the hidden lakes of oil. He fashions a network of highways and sends sleek motor cars to speed over them from sea to sea. Majestic airplanes embody his ideas. He impounds the waters of torrents and harnesses them to the turbine. Arid regions blossom under his touch, and swamps become sites for cities. He runs railroads beneath the ground and highways under the rivers.

Engineering has taken on a new meaning in the twentieth century. More and more attention has been given to conservation and planning. The concept of turning whole regions into laboratories for the engineer is staggering in its significance. Forests have been leveled in an orgy of waste, streams polluted, and fertile soil allowed to wash away. Disastrous floods, terrible dust storms, and fatal droughts have shown clearly the need for large-scale engineering. Mighty rivers, fed by the waters of an inland empire, have scorned their banks to spread devastation. Streams once teeming with fish have been poisoned by refuse. Land once productive has been scarred by gullies and exhausted. Mountains once mantled with extensive forests have been stripped of their trees. This prodigality with natural resources challenges the ingenuity of the engineer to restore them.

When the industrial age gathered momentum, population increased tremendously. At the same time there was a movement from rural regions to urban communities. The result was hundreds of poorly planned cities that sprawled in an ungainly manner over the countryside. City planning is now striving to remedy the mistakes of the past. Architecture is assuming new forms; transportation systems and vehicles are being changed to meet new demands; civic centers are appearing; and there is an unprecedented growth in facilities for recreation. All of these activities will help to make the modern city a work of art, a better place in which to live.

In the ceaseless struggle of man for victory over his environment, the engineer must continue to play a leading role.

J. GARDNER BENNETT

Chicago
January 7, 1938

ACKNOWLEDGMENT

Day and night, year in and year out, on land and sea, in factories, laboratories, mines and homes, and on farms, engineers are continually experimenting with materials, methods, and processes. We have endeavored to tell in pictures this fascinating story of the constant application of engineering to this complex, modern world of ours. We have gone to many sources and called upon numerous individuals and organizations to assist us.

We are particularly grateful to the following persons and groups for their assistance:

The Art Institute of Chicago
Bakelite Corporation
Brewers Journal, Chicago
Charles Bruning Co.
Buffalo Museum of Science
Bureau of Engineering, City of Chicago
Burlington Railroad
Chicago Park District
Chicago Historical Society
Chicago Motor Club
Edwin H. C. Clark
The Container Corporation of America
Robert Crist, Covered Wagon Trailers
Thomas A. Edison, Inc.
Walter H. Flood and Co.
H. M. Gousha Company
Greyhound Bus Lines
Hammond Instrument Co.
Ingersoll-Rand Company
Bureau of Mines Experiment Station, Pittsburgh, Pa.
Museum of Science and Industry, Chicago
Professor D. P. Moreton, Armour Institute of Technology

Mr. J. M. Mercer of the Chicago Sanitary District

Marshall Field and Co., Chicago

National Resources Committee

Tennessee Valley Authority

United States Department of Agriculture, Soil Conservation Service

United States Department of the Interior, Geological Survey

United States Department of Commerce, Coast and Geodetic Survey

United States Lakes Survey

J. BRADFORD PENGELLY
Picture Editor

TABLE OF CONTENTS

MEN AGAINST DARKNESS

THE BATTLE OF THE AGES, the driving back of brute darkness and ignorance by the light of civilization, is chiefly fought by two kinds of men: on one hand, the thinkers and artists; on the other, the doers and builders. Their work is closely knit. Neither could make much progress without the other. If there were no thinkers, the doers and men of action would be no more than savage beasts run mad. If there were no builders, the artists would be no better than lonely dreamers without a language. Moreover, no man is wholly one kind or the other. The person who perfects an intricate, high-speed motor has something of the artist about him; there is beauty in machinery. The sculptor who chisels a massive, towering statue out of marble has a good deal of the engineer in his make-up; the artist must give humanity a beautiful object, a tangible symbol of his dreaming. And so the engineer, the man on whom the spotlight of this book is focused, is more than a mere doer and builder. He is also a thinker, since he makes vital use of the findings of science. He is also an artist, since his work incorporates the great traditions of architectural beauty in particular and of all structural beauty in general.

Imagine what would happen to the world if all building and repairing and devising and constructing came suddenly to an end. Skyscrapers would weather and wear away like the rocks of the Grand Canyon until they finally came crumpling down. Wide transcontinental concrete highways would crack and disintegrate. Cities and towns would be cut off from each other. Piers and docks would break away and obstruct harbors and river mouths. Tracks and wires would rust, making trains and dynamos useless. Houses and farm buildings would rot and fall. Ice and water would make rubbish out of city streets; people would stop using them and weeds and trees would sprout from between the cracks.

Courtesy J. Bradford Pengelly

ANCIENT RUINS AT CORINTH
"The engineer makes use of the findings from all fields of human experience."

Wild beasts would multiply and emerge from the deep forests and come howling to city streets; the domesticated beasts would run wild and join them. Darkness would blot out the bright panorama of civilization; ignorance would win the battle of the ages. Such would be the result if the engineers were eliminated from modern society, if the engineering ability that is an integral part of every man were taken from him.

As the engineer makes use of the findings from all fields of human experience, so, like any other kind of man, he has his special slant and his particular problems. Fairly clear-cut distinctions can be drawn between him and the inventor and the scientist. Concrete illustrations will help to make this plain.

THE ENGINEERS AT WORK

The airplane was invented as the result of the experiments, trials, and failures of a great many men over a long period of time. Yet the work of these many people did not give the desired results until the Wright brothers, using the best combination of ideas, solved the problem. They may be said to be the inventors of the airplane. They went far beyond any previous experimenters.

The Wright brothers were handicapped by the fact that no engine of ample power could be found that was light enough. They also had to find out the best size and shape of the propeller by experimentation. They had to frame their planes with wooden struts and piano wires. Even the problem of a suitable fabric for the wings was not easily solved.

The development of the propeller affords an illustration: when the engineers took up the problem, they had the benefit of a science developed by marine architects, that group of engineers who specialize in the design and construction of ships. These men had long ago discovered the laws of science which apply to the correct and most efficient design of propellers for use on steamships.

The air, engineers reasoned, is a fluid, just as water is. The difference is that air is much lighter and results in considerably less

Paul's Photos, Chicago

THE WRIGHT BROTHERS IN BERLIN

View of an early demonstration given by the Wrights at Tempelhofer Field, Berlin.

friction against a surface moving through it. It is also greatly compressible while water is not. After making corrections for these factors, achievement of the proper design of propellers for airplanes became comparatively easy.

The shape of the wing became important when commercial air lines began to carry passengers. A cabin of some sort was required. From experiments on the flow of water around bridge piers, the engineer was able to find a suitable shape very quickly. Likewise the present shape for the fuselage of planes came into being. And what is the final shape of the present-day planes? The shape of the salmon. The salmon swims long distances against fast-flowing streams. Through centuries nature has been molding his shape to one which has ample room for his organs, float cells, and muscles, but which offers the minimum of resistance to the swift-flowing water through which he moves.

There are two little sermons here. The first is that the engineer always checks his work to be sure it is right. When he noticed similarity to the shape of the salmon, he had his proof. The other lesson is that often the engineer finds that nature has

Courtesy Pan American Airways

CHINA CLIPPER OVER ALCATRAZ ISLAND

solved his problem for him many centuries ago. If he will just look around, he may see the solution.

Thanks to the engineers, planes are now being planned which will fly the Atlantic in about 30 hours. It was found that at certain altitudes weather and air conditions are quite stable. The new planes will be designed with bodies, engines, and propellers especially for use at high altitudes. The engineers know how to make the calculations.

IMPROVING THE AUTOMOBILE

The development of the automobile was similar to that of the airplane. Of course the great corporations now engaged in the manufacture of automobiles are still experimenting, but much of the credit for the availability and general usefulness of the modern car is due the engineers who improved its efficiency and cheapened the cost of its manufacture.

THE OLD AND
THE NEW
MODEL "T" FORD,
1908

A MODERN
STREAM-
LINED SEDAN

Courtesy the
Chrysler Motors
Corporation

Courtesy Ford Motor Co.

ASSEMBLING MOTORS IN AN AUTOMOBILE PLANT

When Henry Ford invented his automobile, most of the design was experimental. He was faced with countless problems. How strong should the axles be? How large should the crankshaft be? Should wood or steel be used for the frame? At what speed would the engine operate most efficiently? How large should the cylinders be? What kind of device would keep the water the coolest? What kind of paint would be the most enduring? And finally, most important of all, could this car be made at a low enough price to sell in large quantities? If it was made at a price so low that the automobile would no longer be a "millionaire's plaything," would the profits of the factory be large enough for the uncertainties and risks involved?

These questions, and many others unthought of in the early days of the industry, have been solved successfully. Applying all branches of science, the engineer has perfected the motor car. No longer do people need a knowledge of machinery and engines to operate an automobile. Even frail people can drive long distances easily and comfortably in automobiles so highly developed that they do almost everything except stop, start, and steer themselves. This development is one of the greatest and finest things ever accomplished by the engineer.

The automotive industry has come a long way from those first handmade engines of Henry Ford, of Haynes, and of Selden. The highly efficient modern gasoline engine has been perfected through the ceaseless, untiring efforts of the engineer. By the use of higher mathematics, and the laws of heat and of burning gases, he has found the ideal size for the cylinders of the engine. It was not an easy problem. Questions of speed had to be considered. This, in turn, involved the availability of suitable materials for the higher speeds proposed. For high efficiency, the gasoline-air mixture in the cylinder must be fired when it is compressed to exactly the proper pressure. Efficiency also required that at this pressure there be a certain definite volume of the gas-air mixture in the cylinder. This raised the question of the volume of space required above each cylinder piston. Another problem that bothered the engineer was the size, number, and spacing of the piston rings which are used to prevent the leakage of gas past the piston.

All these—and they are only a part of the many difficult problems—were solved by the engineer. The space at the top of the cylinder has its volume determined with the same close exactness your druggist uses in measuring out a prescription. The size of the cylinder is made precisely to a thousandth of an inch. Pistons are made of many different metals; they are often of aluminum to reduce the weight and to provide some cushioning by the use of a soft metal. Piston rings are made of strong spring steel, so that they may expand against the walls of the cylinder and yet be free on the piston itself. Very little gas leaks past the rings under the high compressions obtained.

Metallurgical engineers have been active in bringing out metals especially suited for different parts of the modern car. The steel in the fenders must be strong but also soft and malleable. Then if two cars accidentally collide, the dents may be pounded out without spoiling the fender. For the springs the steel must be tough, so that it can be used in very thin strips. The thinner the

AN INSPECTOR TESTING THE ACCURACY OF GEARS

strip, the more it will sway up and down under sudden jolts and impacts. For the cylinders, cast iron is usually used. The metallurgical engineer has found that by adding small amounts of other metals, such as nickel, the alloyed metal will have far greater strength and finer grain, which is to say that when it is machined, the surface of the cuts will be smoother and truer to size and shape.

Metal for the gears has been improved. It is not only stronger, but also wears much better than that used in the early days of the industry. Gears are studied to see where wear occurs and how losses of power may be eliminated. The edge of a gear-tooth is magnified 2500 or 3000 times and projected on a screen. The wear of the tooth shows whether or not the shape is correct and if too much power is being dissipated uselessly in wearing away metal.

THE PARADE OF THE ENGINEERS

The contribution of the engineers to the development of the airplane and automobile is perhaps most remarkable for its versatility. Many fields of knowledge were brought to bear on specific and individual problems. Hydraulic engineers used their knowledge of fluids to perfect the designs of propeller and fuselage. Mechanical engineers improved gasoline motors, giving special attention to each separate part. Metallurgical engineers devised the alloys that rendered each of those separate parts more durable, suitable, and less costly. Still other men gave consideration to fuels and paints, to factory building and assembly methods. There is, indeed, no tight limit to the interests of the engineers, no industry that has not profited in some way by their work. Consider the many names used to designate their fields of specialization: civil engineers, mining engineers, electrical, chemical, and structural engineers; harbor engineers, highway engineers, military, illuminating, and machine tool engineers. All these, added to the ones mentioned before, still do not make up the sum total.

The engineers are the great middlemen of human accomplishment. They are the link between the scientists and inventors on the one hand and the factory owners, farmers, and workers on the other. Problems and difficulties are their province. They are

THE ENGINEER WHO CONCEIVED THE SUEZ CANAL
Fremiet's statue of Ferdinand de Lesseps, French engineer who planned the
Suez Canal (at Port Said, Egypt).

given inventions that practically are little more than toys, and told to make them into something that can be produced and sold in large quantities. They are asked to find a use for waste products, to find some use for the scrap heaps of industry. They are the time savers, the profit makers, the spearheads of competition between rival companies. They are changing the face of the world and shaping the fabric of civilization. The modern factory with its towering walls and roaring machines is not too large a problem for them, or the construction of a cardboard shoe box too small.

GEORGE W. GOETHALS

Paul's Photos, Chicago

HERBERT CLARK HOOVER

International News photo

DESIGNING A SHOE BOX

Follow the shoes from the factory: they are placed in boxes and these boxes in larger containers called cases. Even here nothing is left to chance. The shoe box has been made amply strong and as beautiful and attractive as possible, but it has also been constructed as cheaply as possible. This matter of economy is not merely one of using a machine to save man power in the manufacture; it also involves the selection of the cheapest suitable cardboard. A design must be chosen which will be attractive, catch the eye, and be remembered, but also one which can be cheaply printed. The paper on the outside is carefully chosen. It must look well, help hold the parts together, and resist wear and dirt. Even the wooden cases holding a dozen pairs of shoes in boxes are designed by the engineer.

Engineers have studied the wooden packing case from every

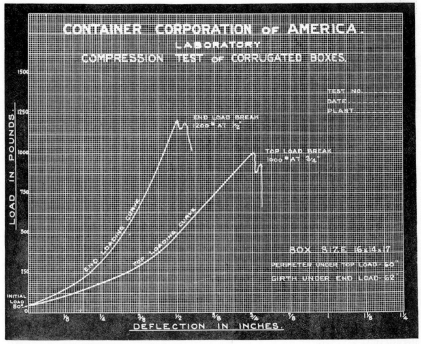

Courtesy Container Corporation of America

AUTOGRAPHIC CHART MADE ON AN OLSON COMPRESSION
TESTING MACHINE

Courtesy Container Corporation of America
PART OF A TYPICAL BOX CONTROL LABORATORY
Inset: A Riehle tester for gaging the force necessary to crush the materials used
in paper box making.

angle. The best sort of wood might be used, but this matter is
governed by the prices of different kinds of wood in various sections of the country. Price is often the governing factor. In
general, the two ends of a packing-case are carefully designed by

men who utilize their knowledge of the strengths of the materials. Factors which must be considered are many. What length of nails should be used? How close together shall they be spaced? Will it be an advantage to coat nails with a cement which sticks to both wood and nail, gluing the nail into the boards? Wood is softer on the sides of the grain than on the ends of the grain. Some sorts of wood split easily. Just how shall the nails be driven with respect to the grain of the wood? If a small nail is used to avoid splitting the boards, will the nail be long enough and strong enough to carry the load?

Some of these questions are answered by using common sense. The answers to others can be calculated. To answer still others, experiments have to be conducted. The container engineers built huge revolving drums, in which were placed boxes filled with goods. As the hollow drum and its load revolved, projections in the drums rolled the boxes back and forth, or held them until they were high on the side and then dropped them to the bottom. Rolling, dropping, banging, the boxes were tested to utter destruction. The results were checked and examined scientifically. As a result of such scientific research, boxes are cheaper, better, and deliver the shoes in better condition.

ENGINEERING THE STORE

Next, consider the store where these shoes are to be sold. Today, a small group of experts are known as store-planning engineers, and their job is to arrange a store in such a manner that the customer is attracted into the various departments by having his curiosity aroused. The store-planner arranges fixtures to display the goods attractively and to catch and hold attention. The proper location of elevators, moving stairways, the candy section, the book section—all are a matter of scientific knowledge to these experts.

Economy is the watchword of the store-planner, just as it is of all engineers. He knows where to put in a large mirror and where to install a small one. He knows where to use light paint and where to use dark paint in surfacing walls and ceilings. In some places indirect illumination is best; in others, exposed lighting fixtures are preferable. In some parts of the store daylight

Courtesy Marshall Field & Co.   Photo by Hedrich-Blessing Studio

ELEVATORS AND ESCALATOR IN A LARGE DEPARTMENT STORE

lamps are needed to display colored materials to their best advantage. Few possibilities which will make a store better looking, attract customers, sell more goods, gain good will, or help the customer to move about the store easily are overlooked. At the same time, the actual handling, unpacking, displaying, wrapping, and delivery of the goods are all carefully planned ahead of time. A properly planned store functions as smoothly on the day it opens as it will a year later.

CONDITIONED AIR

One of the latest developments which make shopping a pleasure, in the summertime especially, is the air conditioning of stores. On hot days the air is chilled and circulated throughout the store; a process which makes it cool and comfortable inside, no matter how warm the weather is outside.

Through scientific planning, the ventilation engineer provides every part of the store with a continuous supply of fresh, clean air. He has found that people enjoy better health and are more comfortable if the air contains the right amount of moisture. Conditioned air is now available to all kinds of public buildings and to private residences.

For many years, methods of air conditioning have been practiced in some of our industries. In many cotton-spinning plants, rooms are maintained at a certain degree of humidity and a narrow range of temperature change in order to keep the fibres soft and pliable.

Public buildings, such as theaters and auditoriums, are now universally air conditioned. When a new theater is to be built, the architect makes his preliminary pictures and sketches rough drafts of the plans. He then calls in the air-conditioning expert to find out how much space will be occupied by machinery and air ducts. Often the refrigeration machinery used to cool the air for one large theater could supply ice for a city of 5,000 people.

In planning theaters the architects also need the services of

Courtesy Owens-Illinois Glass Co.

THE NEW TYPE OF "ROUNDED ARCHITECTURE"
Brick, concrete and glass blocks are combined in this attractive fireproof structure.

another technical expert not as well known to the public at large. He is the acoustics engineer. If an auditorium is well designed, it will be easy to hear the speakers in all parts of the house. The size and shape of the stage and ceiling, the location and number of balconies, the coverings of the walls and the seats, even the clothes of the audience must be considered. An acoustics expert will so shape the ceiling and walls, so hang the decorative drapes that harmful echoes and undesirable absorption of sound will be avoided. Without undue effort a speaker on the stage can then be heard in all parts of the auditorium.

PLANTS AND FACTORIES

In our modern packing plants where animals are slaughtered for food, every effort possible is made to keep all processes sanitary. The meat is cut into the shapes most easily handled. It is stored in refrigerated rooms until it has aged and become tender and well flavored. The process from the time the animal enters the slaughter room until the carcass is hung in the freezing room is continuous. Everywhere the meat moves along on an overhead trolley, most of the time propelled automatically without any assistance from the workmen.

Nothing is wasted in the modern packing plant. All sorts of chemicals are derived from the waste parts. Medicinal preparations are staggering in their number and variety. Food for poultry, fertilizers, glues, casein products, moldable horn, and other products in an amazing profusion are obtained from what would have been wasted at any other period of the world's progress.

It was in the packing plants, where streamlined procession of materials was a simple, logical requirement because of the speed and nature of the operations, that the industrial engineers first learned to plan the steady flow of materials through factories.

Henry Ford realized that the most salable auto would be the one which was not only durable and reliable, but also low in cost. He visited the packing plants and took away with him the idea for his famous assembly lines. Other manufacturers saw its ad-

Courtesy Swift & Company, Chicago

BEEF COOLING ROOM IN A PACKING PLANT

vantages and quickly adopted it. Today, the system that began in the packing industry is used in large production factories the world over.

Most factories are planned by men who specialize in industrial engineering. Many factors influence their selection of a location for a plant. Available supplies of raw materials, provisions for satisfactory living conditions for the workers, good shipping facilities, nearness to markets, competition of other companies, and space for future expansion are studied thoroughly. The advantages of possible locations are compared carefully. Perhaps one of them has lower taxes—that may be the deciding factor in making the choice.

When available land in a suitable city has been found, a map of the land is made and the buildings are built. The factory is designed so that raw materials come in at one gate of the plant, pass quickly through a hundred different operations and processes and come out at the other end finished products ready to be loaded

Courtesy Swift & Company, Chicago

DRESSING SHEEP IN A PACKING PLANT

on freight cars or trucks. The operations have been arranged in sequence so that materials move forward through the successive processes with a minimum of handling.

Labor-saving devices are developed and used where they will prove economical by paying for themselves and returning a good profit on the money invested in them. An example of such a machine is the "nailing" machine, which drives thirty-six rivets in the frame of an automobile in almost less time than it takes to read about it. The parts of the frames have been pressed into shape and tacked together with a few rivets to hold them in position. When the partly finished frame has been placed on the riveting machine, a man pulls a lever and rat-ta-tat-tat, the rivets are clinched into every hole on the frame. In an instant, it is all over, and the frame is ready to be painted. Another frame is already in place waiting for the riveter. The machine moves as swiftly as the engineers intended it to move.

BUILDERS OF YESTERDAY, TODAY, AND TOMORROW

When the cave man first used an axe, built a log raft, bent a bow, or used a lever to crack juicy marrow bones, he was something of an engineer. Broadly speaking, there are two essential respects in which man differs from all other animals. He has a language, and he has mechanical ability. Man might well be called the animal which can communicate his thoughts and take premeditated advantage of the forces of nature. Past ages have seen a succession of builders and artificers: Egyptians who built the kingly tombs of austere lines that are the pyramids; Phoenicians who dared the seas in their trim galleys; the Romans who webbed their civilization with roads; the Chinese who raised the Great Wall against barbarianism; the Mohammedans who used the compass to chart dangerous coastlines; the makers of the cathedrals, the temples, and the mosques. By his mechanical ability and by his language man raised himself above the brute, slowly winning more and more power for himself and his own.

Every man has something of the engineer in him; however, for centuries engineering was not looked upon as an especially honorable or noble profession in itself. To be leaders of road-working gangs, foremen in mines, workmen, toilers—such was the fate of the men who were nothing but engineers. Julius Caesar was a great engineer, designing bridges very much lighter in weight than had ever been successfully built before, but that was not the reason for his greatness in Roman society. Today, however, the engineers are riding with the scientists and liberators on the crest of the wave of human popularity. All industry is their profession. Their eyes are fixed on the future. If a list be made of their activities, the engineers cry: "Not enough! Not enough! We are doing more things than that. Every day the horizon of our work widens. Look! Look!"

Indeed, the only fitting way to discuss the engineers is to present once again concrete examples of the variety of their interest. The sanitary engineer, the hydraulic engineer, the engineer of organic processes, and the electrical engineer will be considered.

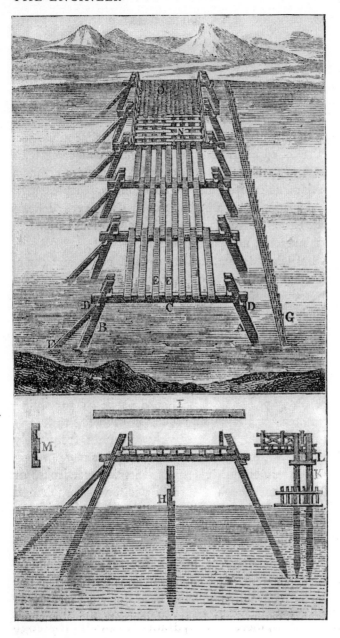

PLAN OF CAE-
SAR'S BRIDGE
ACROSS THE
RHINE, BUILT
IN 10 DAYS

A: two piles, each
one and one-half
feet thick, joined
together about
two feet apart;
B: opposite piles
similarly joined;
C: large beam
between piles;
D: braces; E:
cross timbers; F:
buttress stakes
sunk in river; G:
fences to protect
the bridge from
floating trees,
etc.; H: form of
beams one and
one-half feet
thick; I: cross-
beam; K, figure
showing the two
piles braced to-
gether; L: braces;
M: detached
brace; N: spare
laid athwart; O:
hurdles.

Courtesy Bureau of Engineering, City of Chicago

SECTION OF A MODERN FILTRATION PLANT

THE SANITARY ENGINEER

Sanitary engineers are charged with the work of supplying water to cities. Those who specialize in this phase of the task may be called hydraulic engineers but probably are more frequently called water works engineers.

In the olden days great faith was placed in water witches or diviners who could go out with a forked stick, walk back and forth and finally locate a spot where a well would furnish an abundant supply of good water.

Sometimes the modern water works engineer seems almost as mysterious. When he is commissioned to design a water works system for a small city, his first step is to find the water supply. If no spring or lake, or suitable river sources are found, ground water will have to be sought. A study of the geology of the region shows him just how deep the water will be. He can also prophesy the chemicals which will be found in solution and other characteristics of the water.

In case a surface water supply, such as a lake or a river, is used, the water is usually treated to remove harmful bacteria, and other objectionable substances such as mud, odors, colors. In some cities the water supply must be treated to remove those chemicals which make the water hard. Hardness in water is objectionable because deposits of lime and other minerals are formed in boilers, tea kettles, and water heaters, and housewives must use an increased amount of soap to clean fabrics. Generally, where the water is hard, the saving in soap bills is sufficient to pay more than the cost of removing the hardness at the water works.

Most water treatment plants work on the same principle— the production of a flaky deposit called *floc*, which can be filtered

Courtesy Bureau of Engineering, City of Chicago

CHLORINE OPERATING ROOM AT CERMAK PUMPING STATION, CHICAGO, SHOWING CHLORINATORS AND RECORDING WEIGHING SCALES

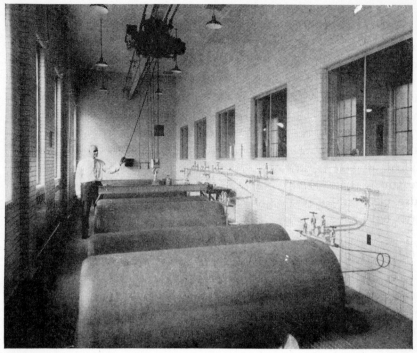

Courtesy Bureau of Engineering, City of Chicago

CHLORINE CONTAINERS AT CERMAK PUMP STATION, CHICAGO

out of the water. Generally this is done by the use of chemicals. Alum, and sometimes lime, soda ash, and iron sulphate are among the chemicals which can be added to the water in such quantities as are necessary to counteract the varying hardness of the water. In some instances, cities use a deep tank in which the water and the chemicals are stirred until a complete mixing is accomplished. From the mixing tank, the water goes to a large vat where the insoluble particles are allowed to settle. As the heavy floc sinks, it carries down with it most of the harmful and disease-bearing bacteria. The small amounts of the finer particles of floc that do not settle are carried off in the water which goes to the filters.

The filter bed consists of about three feet of sand and gravel in layers. The finest sand is on top. As the depth of sand increases, the material becomes coarser. The layer above the drains is entirely composed of coarse gravel. The floc and other fine material in the water soon form a coating, or layer, on the top of the filter bed which strains out even the very finest particles. The water running from the bottom of the filter is clear and for all practical purposes entirely pure.

As an additional precaution, to insure a sterile water, small quantities of liquid chlorine gas are added before it is pumped into the distributing system of pipes.

The results of water treatment are quite astounding. At St. Louis and New Orleans water from the Mississippi River, muddy, full of silt and slime, is pumped into the treatment plant. After treatment the water is fairly soft, free from odor and color, and is pure, clear, and sparkling. More than a million people in these two cities use this water daily.

THE HYDRAULIC ENGINEER

Hydraulic engineers, however, are concerned with the construction of many other projects besides water works and treatment plants. One group of hydraulic engineers is concerned with the irrigation of land. Another group is interested in building dams for power. Still others are draining swamps. Some may be digging canals and deepening rivers and harbors for navigation.

Each of these engineers has specialized in answering certain important questions. Consider those of the irrigation expert. Is the land flat enough to carry irrigation ditches? What crops can be raised? How much will it cost to ship these crops to markets? Are there good locations for towns and cities? How much can a farmer afford to pay for water and all his other needs and still make a profit on his crops? How much water is required to raise one acre of these crops? Where will this water come from? How much water is available? Can the amount be increased by building a dam to impound water during the wet months? Just what is the minimum amount of useful water that can be counted on in the driest years? How will this water be conducted to the fields: by canals, metal or wooden flumes, or pipes? What will be the cost of the dam, the canals, and the flumes? How much will have to be spent to keep them in repair? Will the project pay for itself?

Similar questions arise in all hydraulic engineering projects. Consider the matter of flood prevention: in Ohio, Dayton and the Miami River Valley are protected by large reservoirs which retard the heavy floods and make them flow down the valley so slowly that the banks of the river are not overrun. The cost of the entire project was enormous, yet it was lower than the probable cost of trying to move the cities of Dayton, Middletown, Hamilton, and others out of the valley onto higher ground.

The small city of Shawneetown, Illinois, furnishes the other extreme in flood prevention. It was found to be cheaper to move this city several miles away than to try to build levees high enough to prevent the Ohio River from flooding it. In these days, when automobiles are very common, there is not a great deal of opposition to such a thing as moving a small city. Good roads make it as easy for farmers to get to one site as to the other.

Courtesy Union Pacific Railroad

A STRIKING VIEW OF BOULDER DAM

Courtesy Caterpillar Tractor Co.

A TRACTOR DITCHER IN OPERATION

Courtesy Brewers Journal, Chicago

SECTION OF A LABORATORY IN A BREWING PLANT

ENGINEERING ORGANIC PROCESSES

The farmer's grains are used by the chemical engineer in brewing beers and distilling liquors. In this case, the grain is sorted carefully and only the best is used. The processes are not only mechanical and chemical; the engineer uses also biochemistry. In order to produce alcohol, fermentation must be induced. Microorganisms in the form of yeast spores are mixed with grain which has previously been soaked, steamed, and mashed to soften it and force out the starch. They ferment the starches in the grains, turning them into alcohol, as well as carbon dioxide gas, which is compressed and used to carbonate the effervescent water of soda fountains. When the fermentation has reached the right stage, the grain is run through rollers to squeeze out every drop of liquid. The pulp that is left is called malt.

Malt has a few medicinal uses but it is chiefly employed as feed for cattle. The liquid removed from it, however, is put through a still to take out the alcohol. Then an exactly predetermined amount of alcohol is returned to the liquor. Hops and other ingredients may be added to give flavor and color. If the biochemist has added hops, he now has beer. The product is stored in cooled rooms, and aged in large vats, thereby improving the flavor, completing any fermentation, and removing impurities that may be objectionable.

In making whiskeys, no hops are added and a higher percentage of alcohol is found in the finished liquor. Along with the alcohol, a number of rather objectionable impurities are left. These are removed in the old-fashioned manner by aging the whiskey in barrels of oak, the insides of which have been burned to charcoal. In time the oak and charcoal remove the objectionable impurities and improve the flavor. The longer the whiskey is aged, the less the unwanted impurities and the better the flavor.

The biochemical engineer is also employed in other industries. He uses bacteria to ripen, flavor, and cure cheeses. The large holes in Swiss cheese have long been a source of jokes for humorists. But the way these holes are made is even funnier than the professional humorist imagines. After the Swiss cheese has been

NEW TYPE OF
MALT MILL
This machine re-
moves dust and for-
eign matter from the
malt, and crushes it
for brewing.

Courtesy Brewers
Journal, Chicago

molded to shape, it is soaked in a salt brine solution until a rind
has actually been tanned on all the outside surface of the cheese.
Then each cheese is inoculated in several spots with a bacterial
culture which later gives it the right flavor and causes a gas to be
formed which collects and makes the holes. If the inoculation
has been carefully done, the holes will be large and well distributed. They will be shiny with perhaps just a trace of moisture
present when the cheese is first cut open.

The inoculation with cultivated bacteria is done by means
of an instrument that is something like a hypodermic needle—
much like that used on human beings in making prophylactic
inoculations. The cheese is put away to cure for several months,
and if the humidity and temperature are kept just right, the bacteria will find their surroundings favorable for rapid growth and
development.

A similar use of bacteria is the introduction of mold-forming
micro-organisms into what becomes Roquefort cheese. Many

other cheeses famous in different parts of the world owe their distinct flavors and textures to the bacteria present and to the conditions under which the cheese was cured.

Given good milk, a choice of equipment, and suitable rewards, the biochemical engineers in the dairy industry can make almost any sort of cheese in any part of the world.

ELECTRICITY—THE UNIVERSAL SERVANT

Even more astonishing is the miracle of electricity. The electrical engineer has made it possible to talk across the ocean without the use of wires. He has built equipment capable of sending more than sixty telephone conversations over one hollow wire,

FERMENTING TANKS IN A MODERN BREWERY

Courtesy Brewers Journal, Chicago

in addition to a few telegraph messages in each direction, all at the same time.

Using electronic tubes, the engineer sorts beans. As the beans pass by on a belt, the machine picks out all that are not of standard color and size. Photoelectric cells are used to count the number of automobiles passing a given point in a tunnel. They are placed at the entrances of elevators to prevent the doors from accidentally closing on a passenger. In factories, they measure steel for size, thickness, and freedom from distortion, doing this difficult job steadily and more reliably than a human being.

Amplifying tubes are an important part of radio sets. They are also used on long-distance telephone lines. Each fifty miles or so, there is one of these tubes which boosts the current carrying the message. They are not the identical tube found in the radio but belong to the same general class.

THE ELECTRIC ORGAN

As a final example of the wonders of modern electrical engineering, consider the electric organ. It does everything a pipe organ can do and a great many other things. It sends out its tones over a loud speaker. It is light, occupies little space, and is portable. It can be moved around as easily as a piano. The amount of current required is small, and it may be plugged into any ordinary lamp socket.

The development of the electric organ is illustrative of the engineer's debt to science. From a knowledge of the frequencies and shapes of sound waves, from a knowledge of the manner in which the modern radio tubes change minute electrical impulses into sound, and from a scientific study of musical tones and harmony, the engineer was able to plan and build a machine from which almost any tone or combination of tones could be produced. He adapted the device to the standard organ keyboard and made it a familiar instrument to a pipe-organist.

THE CONTRIBUTIONS OF THE ENGINEER

The engineer has given flashing airplanes and automobiles to the world in which we live. He has lightened the work of the

Courtesy Hammond Instrument Co.

CONSOLE AND AMPLIFIER OF AN ELECTRIC ORGAN
The cabinet under the window resembling a radio contains the amplifying
apparatus of the organ.

laborer in farm and factory and home. He keeps our cities neat and clean and furnishes us pure sparkling water priced so reasonably that we use it to sprinkle our lawns. He brings entertainment to shut-in radio listeners, draws music from the electric organ, and diverts us with talking motion pictures.

Thanks to the engineer, an abundance of good food is brought from the far corners of the earth, arriving as fresh as the day it was packed. People wear clothes of good fabric made by well-housed workers in comfortable factories. The miner in frigid Alaska lives in a comfortably heated house, while the superintendent of a rubber plantation in the jungles of torrid Brazil relaxes in a cool, air-conditioned home. Unused materials such as short cotton fiber and wood chips are digested by acids, cooked, and finally spun into wisps of rayon, stronger, more lustrous, and more beautiful, than natural silk. The engineer has given us a material culture never before known.

The engineer has placed the devices of the inventor within the reach of us all, at a profit, to be sure, but at a price we can afford to pay. Upon his shoulders rests a titanic responsibility. It is his fate to be one of the leaders in the unending fight against ignorance and darkness. It is his duty to be one of the wisest.

ENGINEERING KNOWLEDGE—A TOOL

Generally speaking, no great science or useful art is the work of one man, or even of a small group of men. For every Aristotle, Newton, Leibnitz, or Einstein there is a host of little known or unknown investigators and thinkers whose work helped to make the work of the great masters both possible and significant. Against the great individual sculptors of the Renaissance stand the ghostly ranks of anonymous artists and artisans who adorned the spired cathedrals of Europe. Little men stand on the shoulders of great men, but great men stand on the shoulders of little men too. Insofar as this is true of science and art, it is even more true of engineering, which has an inalienable right to be called the universally useful art, the practical science of the people, by the people, and for the people.

Every man works with materials; every man is an engineer.

Indeed, we have defined man as an animal with engineering ability—engineering ability and language. From the days of the first crude levers and baskets, the first rollers and the first wedges, the sum of engineering knowledge has been steadily growing. Many humble workmen have added significant innovations and improvements; the modern engineer often remains as anonymous as the man who initially shaped the wheel. Whole nations and peoples have left their imprint on the body of engineering knowledge. It is not the monopoly of any one culture or any limited society. The arch and the column, the plow and the sword, the road and the mine have been transmitted from age to age and from culture to culture, independent of language, politics, religion, and theoretical science. Engineering knowledge is not the miraculous gift of modern professionals but the accumulated and still accumulating heritage of the ages.

Further, it is a material heritage, not a spiritual one. It is a record of man's skill in fashioning and using materials, and not until recently has it taken consideration of esthetic values that are inherent in all men's work. Man's engineering knowledge is a tool; and, as all other tools, it is useful when it is put to work at a task. That task may be for good or ill, war or peace, destructiveness as well as constructiveness. Directive intelligence will always be needed if the works of engineering knowledge are to contribute to the welfare of the human brotherhood.

Courtesy Burlington Railroad

ENTRANCE TO MOFFAT TUNNEL

MEASURING—ONE OF THE OLDEST ARTS

M OST OF US, at some time or another in our lives, have seen a man peering through an instrument set on a tripod. He is not taking pictures, as some of us might have imagined, but he is "surveying." His instrument is not a camera, but a special kind of telescope, so constructed that he can determine the distances to various points. This "surveyor" is practicing an art that must have existed for almost as long as man can remember. Popular belief has it that the Egyptians were the first surveyors. There is a papyrus on file at the British Museum that gives rules for calculating areas of triangles, trapezoids, and circles. This papyrus is supposed to have been written about 1700 B.C.; it is a monument of ancient ingenuity.

We are told that the Romans, when they were engaged in extensive road building for their military campaigns, used surveying to keep those roads properly aligned and on the most convenient routes. Many of the ancient roads were so well laid out and constructed that they are still in use. Another evidence of early surveying is found in a book by Hero of Alexandria mentioning the art of planning the underground passages in mines.

We have often marveled at the stupendous engineering feats of the people of ancient Greece, Egypt, and other civilizations. These people, with no apparent knowledge of such engineering principles as we have today, erected huge pyramids and temples that would tax the ingenuity of many a modern engineer. A study of the measurements of the Great Pyramid shows that the early Egyptians had knowledge of the art of surveying.

An investigation of the methods of irrigation in the vicinity of the Nile River affords more evidence of ancient surveying knowledge. The dirt-banked canals sometimes extended for miles away

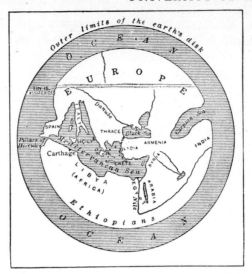

HECATAEUS' MAP OF THE WORLD, 517 B.C.

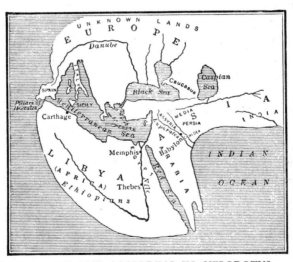

A WORLD MAP ACCORDING TO HERODOTUS

from the great, silty river and it was necessary that correct measurements of distance and elevation be made to assure the success of the system. Those early cultivators of grain also knew that water could not flow uphill—even though they may not have known why—hence it was necessary that the canal beds never exceeded the river in elevation. A knowledge of measurement of distance was important so that when the diggers had finished their work they would end up at the right place. The men of the Nile also constructed maps of their projects, but they were quite different from our maps of today. The symbols were mostly pictures, or hieroglyphics, having a special meaning to the people of those early days, just as the symbols on present-day maps have certain meanings to us.

FINDING BURIED GOLD

Do you remember your childhood days when nothing was quite as exciting as a good hair-raising pirate mystery thriller? Perhaps you also remember that such a story was not quite complete unless it contained at least one map that showed the location of the buried pirate booty. These old pirates, although their vocations were far from being scientific, practiced surveying when they made the maps that enabled them to relocate their treasure. They used one of the fundamental principles of surveying, namely "pacing." Usually those pirate maps contained directions to walk "twenty paces north of the crooked stump," and so on. The measuring of distance by pacing is possible because every person has a normal walking gait. That is, every step taken when walking normally is of fairly uniform length, usually a little under three feet. A "stride," or a step with each foot, is from five to six feet. People of earlier generations undoubtedly resorted to this means of measuring distances, if for no other reason than that measuring instruments were few and far from the standards of present-day precision.

The crudities of old-time maps are very evident to us as we compare them with the scientifically accurate ones of the present day. Perhaps you have seen some ancient maps that portray the countries that now form modern Europe. If so, you will

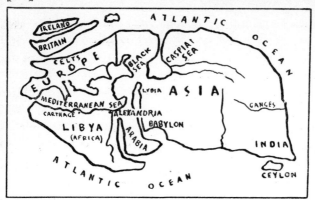

MAP OF EUROPE,
ASIA AND AFRI-
CA ACCORDING
TO ERATOS-
THENES, ALEX-
ANDRIAN GEOG-
RAPHER

have noticed that all the bodies of water were adorned with huge and grotesque-appearing fish and other forms of sea life. If you should place one of those old maps beside a modern map of Europe, you would hardly recognize the two as representing the same countries. This may be attributed to errors resulting from crude measuring practices, and difficulties encountered because of lack of transportation and necessary fundamental knowledge. Undoubtedly, much of the map-making bordered on guesswork.

Only in the past few centuries has it been universally known that the earth is round. This fact alone may account for many of the errors of early map-making. The curvature of the earth is a very important point that must be taken into account when a map representing any vast amount of land is being made. We ordinarily think of a line parallel with the earth as being straight, when actually it is not. Although the line appears straight, it is really a part of a circle conforming to the shape of the earth. The correction that must be made is seven to eight inches per mile. This small error may be neglected when short distances are being measured, but in a big project, such as a map of the United States, the failure to make this correction of seven to eight inches per mile would result in giving Canada three-fourths of the state of Washington.

Along with the fact that early people had only crude distance-measuring equipment to use, their direction-finding instruments were nothing compared to ours of today. They had compasses that were successful enough, it is true, but the very fact that there are only a very few places on the earth where a compass will point to true north may have caused some of the queer-looking maps of the past. The north pole that attracts the needle of a compass is not the North Pole of the earth. There will be quite a few degrees' difference, depending on the location of the compass on the earth. The difference in these magnetic readings is not always constant either, but that is a subject too complicated to discuss here.

The Arabs of about 1450 A.D. are generally credited with being the first to use compasses in map-making. On journeys to countries they visited, they used these compasses to chart coastlines. Their charting was not always correct because of the crude types of instruments they used.

HOW AN ARMY TRAVELS

Aside from the "civil" uses of surveys and maps, such as proposed or already constructed buildings, bridges, roads, railways, etc., one of the most important phases of surveying is its use from a military standpoint.

If a military campaign is to be successful, it is absolutely essential that the engineering must be as highly efficient as possible. This efficiency may be attained through knowledge of the territory in which military operations are being conducted. It is necessary to show on maps all hills, streams, valleys, roads, railroads, buildings, woods, and other details of the territory in question. The success or failure of a campaign may depend on any one or more of these features. Surveys must be conducted before suitable camps can be erected. Here provision must be made for housing and sanitation. A survey will determine the best location just as it will in the offensive or defensive operations of an army.

The engineers are also responsible for the movement of troops over the most advantageous routes and for communications between troops and headquarters. The construction of the most successful type of defense line, depending on the condition of the country, can be determined by a survey of the territory. Locations of siege works are also decided in this manner. Underground communication systems have been used in the past and surveys must be made to insure their success. The location of these underground systems must be known and also the best methods of reaching them. Bridges and roads over which troops are to be moved can be constructed to best advantage if accurate surveys are available.

Military strategy received quite a helping hand during the World War when it became possible to photograph enemy territory from airplanes. The nature of the territory was thus learned, and in some instances enemy movements could be anticipated. These photographs often revealed enemy ammunition dumps and positions of troops. It was possible to figure the most successful kind of attack when through these photographs such knowledge was gained of the type of country in which the enemy was located. The success of many military campaigns has depended upon such information.

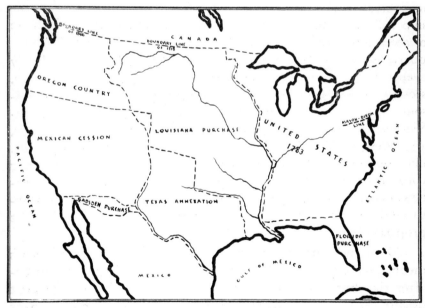

IMPORTANT EARLY SURVEYS OF THE UNITED STATES, SHOWING
THE FAMOUS MASON-DIXON LINE

The Army engineers made the first surveys of any importance in the United States. Much of the country was unsurveyed until comparatively recent times, and many exploring parties gained renown because of the geographical surveys they made. Many of these surveys and those conducted by army engineers have formed the groundwork on which present land allotments and township divisions are made.

FINDING YOUR WAY HOME

Few of us who own property have ever given much thought to the part played by the surveyor in the matter of land ownership. Every lot in a city or farm in the country has very definite boundaries that have been established by means of surveying, and this information is all duly recorded. These particular character-istics of land ownership are invaluable should any sort of dispute arise concerning boundaries, areas, or locations.

The major parcels of land are divided into townships which, in general, contain thirty-six square miles of land. The town-ship has thirty-six sections, each approximately one mile square or six hundred and forty acres. The sections are divided into four quarter-sections and these are further divided by eight until eventually we reach the individual lot, in the case of a residence section. The description of a farmer's property, for example, may sound something like this: "The Northeast Quarter (NE ¼) of Section Thirteen (13), Township Eight (8) South, Range Three (3) West, of the Initial Point of the Fifth (5) Principal Merid-ian, containing one hundred sixty (160) acres, more or less, ac-cording to the United States Survey." That may sound rather bewildering, but it is information which will enable a surveyor to establish definitely the location and boundaries of a piece of property.

All of these descriptions involve the use of accurate measure-ments over great distances. This measuring is called "chaining," after the practice of using chains with links of definite length, usually .66 of a foot made into a chain of one hundred links. However, this method was proved to be inaccurate for modern purposes, and steel tapes are now used to measure off distances.

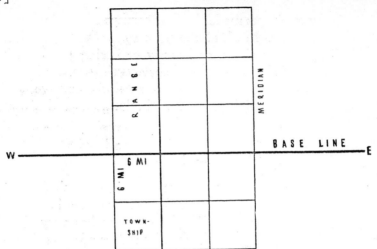

SYSTEM OF LAND SURVEY

Township map showing sections and sub-divisions. A, Section, 640 acres; B, half section; C, quarter section; D, half quarter section; E, quarter quarter section (40 acres).

SURVEYORS'
TRANSIT

Courtesy Charles Bruning Co.

These tapes come in lengths from fifty to five hundred feet, with the one hundred feet lengths proving the most popular for ordinary purposes.

Taping lines are kept straight by lining up the "tape" on each measurement by means of a telescope device called a "transit." The instrument is set at the proper angle, along the line to be measured, and the men measuring with the "tape" can be directed in a straight line by the man operating the transit. When he looks through the telescope, which has been set at a definite angle, he sees a vertical cross hair. He directs the "tapemen" by means of arm signals, if they are out of hearing distance, to shift the tape back or forth for each measurement until the steel tape is "cut" right down its long axis by the telescope's vertical cross hair. This eliminates the possibility of the tape being laid in a zig-zag fashion when the distance to be measured is greater than the length of the tape.

Measurements are usually begun from a definitely established point, called a "reference point," "bench mark," or "initial point." These points are identified by some permanent object, such as a small stone marker, fire plug, a point on a bridge pier, and so on. The use of a reference point may be illustrated by finding a point on a piece of paper. Suppose you were instructed to locate a point four inches to the right and three inches below the upper left hand corner of a sheet of paper. Here, the upper left hand corner is used as a "reference point." Another point or mark on the paper would not be a wise choice, because it may be obliterated, but the upper left hand corner is fairly permanent. So it is with such points in the field. A tree would not be a good reference point, because it might be chopped down and the point would become lost. The selection of a new one would involve inconvenience, expense, and delay, hence the normal practice is to use objects of a permanent nature for such reference points.

The natural features of land are of help oftentimes to the surveyor in his work. Peaks of hills may be used to obtain bearings or reference points, and natural boundaries such as rivers are often an aid in the location of a particular piece of land.

Courtesy Charles Bruning Co.

SURVEYOR'S LEVEL

MOVING MOUNTAINS

Many people who are interested in the welfare of nations have said that rivers, mountains, etc., were placed to keep different peoples apart. Others are of the belief that such natural boundaries serve to bring peoples more closely together. Good arguments may be found to substantiate both theories, but the fact remains that these topographic features have served for centuries as boundaries between tribes, first of all, and then nations.

As man increased his storehouse of knowledge, however, these difficulties have gradually been overcome; first in a small way, such as learning to cross a small stream, and more recently in a large way, such as boring a railroad tunnel through the solid rock of a mountain.

Surveying, of course, has been the main reason that such natural barriers have been knocked down, so to speak. When a bridge, tunnel, railroad, or highway is to be built, the first thing that must be done is to have surveys made of many tentative sites. From these surveying observations are drawn maps, on which are noted all features of topography, such as hill, plains, woods, streams; and even the kind of ground, marsh, sand, rock, or whatever it may be. Such maps are called "topographic maps," because they illustrate the topography of the territory in question, or the "lay of the land." A final decision is made on one of these tentative sites, and that becomes the one that will be used for the construction of the project. After all the designs have been made, the surveyor is again needed when actual work begins. It is his duty to see that the bridge or whatever it may be being constructed is in exactly the right spot. He must line up the piers and abutments even as work is progressing to make sure that their location will be exact and proper. Then, when the bridge itself is being built, he must be at his instruments to see that each part of the bridge is at the proper elevation. If the bridge is being built from both shores at the same time, it would be costly to have the two ends meet in the middle of the river with one end two or three feet higher or lower than the other. They must meet exactly.

Courtesy Union Pacific Railroad

AN AIR VIEW OF BOULDER DAM

During the construction of the Moffat railroad tunnel west of Denver, an amazing engineering feat occurred. The tunnel is slightly more than six miles long and digging was started from both ends. The tunnel floor rose on a .3% grade from the eastern entrance toward the center, and descended on an .8% and .9% grade toward the western entrance. So exact were the engineers' measurements and so precise was the guidance of surveyors that when the two digging parties met in the center, the center lines of the two bores were only a fraction of an inch apart, yet both parties had to dig over three miles before meeting each other.

Another amazing achievement in surveying took place during preparation for the construction of Boulder Dam. It was necessary to draw maps of the area, particularly the canyon walls, against which the dam would be seated. These walls were a sheer drop of hundreds of feet down to the Colorado River which snaked its way through the canyons. This meant that "rodmen" would have to get on the walls in some way. These rodmen carried rods which were like huge rulers with graduations in feet and decimals of a foot. The transit, or telescope, man, took sights or "shots" at this rod for his distance measurements. Even an expert Alpine Mountain climber would find it almost impossible to scale such a wall, so these rodmen were lowered over the side from the top, like buckets down a well, by means of cables. Then the operator of the cable could move them to the side of the wall and the transitman could take his readings. Very often these rodmen would start swinging like a huge pendulum and crash against the face of the wall, but their job was to measure the walls and this they did efficiently.

AN EASY WAY TO DO DIFFICULT WORK

Triangulation is a very important and widely used form of surveying. This is a system by which a maximum of angular measurements in the determination of distances and directions is possible with a minimum of measured distance. The basic principle of the method is, as its name indicates, the use of triangles and their areas. Oftentimes, in engineering surveys, it is neces-

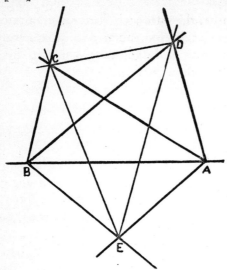

TRIANGULAR NET USED IN
SURVEYING

sary to secure the distance across a canyon or a body of water. Obviously tape measuring is impractical, so triangulation must be used.

Another fundamental principle of this system is the trigonometric fact that of the six parts of a triangle, three angles and three sides, only three must be known beforehand, providing at least one is a side, for the determination of the other three. In triangulation, one side of the triangle will always be known, because a base line is laid off and measured between the two transits that are to sight the same point across the canyon or body of water. Each transit will have its angular reading set at 0° when it is sighted along the base line, then it is swung through an arc and trained on the point in question. This will provide two angular measurements and one distance measurement—the three factors necessary for the solution of the other angle and two distances. The third angle of the triangle may be found by subtracting the sum of the two known angles from 180°, since the three angles of every triangle, regardless of its shape, add up to 180°. The two remaining unknown sides can be solved by a simple trigonometric formula.

The more elaborate systems of triangulation employ networks of triangles, that is, the triangles assume a shape much as a series of rough rectangles drawn on end, with each rectangle containing diagonals. These series of triangles afford a comparatively easy method of determining areas of large spaces, such as long stretches of coast lines, or even whole state

THE GOVERNMENT SURVEYS

This type of work is very common with the United States Coast and Geodetic Survey, a bureau of the Department of Commerce. Their work consists in surveying large areas and involves also the principles of geodesy, the most important of which takes into consideration the curvature of the earth. It has been previously mentioned that this curvature amounts to between seven and eight inches per mile. Hence, it can readily be seen what serious error would result if this factor were not given consideration.

The main function of the United States Coast and Geodetic survey is to chart all coast lines and to publish the charts. Such features as the condition of the bottom of the sea, locations of reefs and shoals, rise and fall of tides, direction and strength of currents, and many other items are of vast importance to those connected with the sea. This branch of surveying was begun when President Jefferson sent F. R. Hassler to Europe in 1811 to obtain the necessary equipment to start the work. Congress appropriated $150,000 to get it under way. The war between England and the United States broke out shortly after Mr. Hassler's trip, and he was compelled to remain on the continent for some time, finally returning to this country in 1815.

The work of coastal surveying was actually started in August of the next year, and the work was confined chiefly to the vicinity of New York City until 1818.

The bureau was a political football until about 1832, being shunted about, under the jurisdiction first of one governmental department and then of another. Work was resumed, however, in 1833, with Mr. Hassler still in charge, and up to 1843 an area of about 9,000 square miles had been surveyed by the triangulation system. There were 1,200 stations along the coast line delineating 1,600 miles of shore line.

Courtesy U. S. Coast and Geodetic Survey

Courtesy U. S. Coast and Geodetic Survey

TIDE STATION AT ANCHORAGE, ALASKA

Low wa er reading 7½ feet on the tide staff.

THE ANCHORAGE, ALASKA, TIDE STATION

High water reading 41 feet on tide staff.

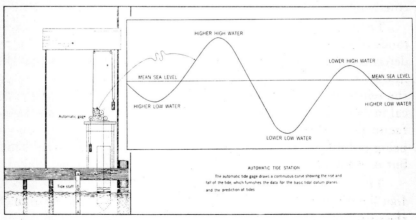

Courtesy U. S. Coast and Geodetic Survey

GRAPH SHOWING TIDE STATION AND TYPICAL TIDE CURVE AS TRACED BY THE AUTOMATIC GAGE

The advent of the Civil War again halted the bureau's activities and most of its officers were drafted into the service of the northern fleet. Their knowledge of the coast and experience in this type of work proved to be invaluable aids to the northern ships in their naval operations.

At the present time, however, the bureau is under the jurisdiction of the Department of Commerce. A superintendent heads the entire bureau and he is responsible only to the Secretary of Commerce.

HOW FAR CAN YOU STEP

The prime purpose of surveying is to determine the relative locations on the earth's surface of points and lines. These factors, in most cases, are recorded on maps, but the reverse procedure is also just as important, namely, locating points and lines on the ground that have already been depicted on a surveyor's map. These locations involve measuring distance on the ground and above or under the ground. The first essential thing to learn, however, is the measurement of distance.

Pacing, as mentioned before, is the most elementary form, and is accurate within about two per cent. This system is practical when rough estimates are to be made, or in the event of an emergency, when no other measuring instruments are available.

The speedometer of an automobile may also be used as a distance measuring instrument. The nearest tenth of a mile can be determined by this system, or it may be refined to read to the nearest hundredth of a mile if proper lines are recorded between the tenth-of-a-mile marks. Obviously, this system is only practical in fairly level territory over which an automobile can be satisfactorily operated. This method is more accurate than pacing, it being possible to achieve results with only one-half per cent error, but it is not advisable to use it except for rough estimates.

The use of steel tapes in from one-hundred- to five-hundred-foot lengths is the most accurate form of measurement of distance the surveyor has at his command. Fifty-foot lengths are also available but are not common among surveyors, being used chiefly by mechanics, builders, and installers of machinery.

Courtesy Charles Bruning Co.

THE WORLD'S OLDEST TRANSIT

Said to be the oldest transit in existence, his instrument, hand made in 1723, is owned by Ralph Maybee, Des Moines, Iowa. It has no magnifier and all readings were made by cross hairs.

The steel tape was preceded by a method known as "chaining." This was done with a chain composed of one hundred links, each link being about 0.66 of a foot, or 7.92 inches long. The system was known as the "surveyor's" or "Gunter's chain." The word "chain" was also applied to a unit of sixty-six feet, which is still used in referring to surveys of sections of land. The United States General Land Office records and measures distances as eighty "chains" equaling one mile and ten square chains equaling one acre.

The actual use of chains was practiced until the end of the nineteenth century, when they were abandoned in favor of the more easily handled steel tape. The term "chaining," however, is still retained but is losing favor; it is often replaced by the use of such words at "taping" and "tapemen."

The method of reading distance by "stadia" is an important part of surveying. Under certain conditions it compares favorably, in regard to accuracy, with the taping system. The equipment includes a "transit" and a "stadia" rod on which are marked feet and various decimals of feet. For short "shooting" up to three hundred or four hundred feet, the rods are graduated into hundredths of a foot. Rods of coarser graduation, usually tenths of a foot, are used when sighting longer distances. Some instrumentmen prefer rods graduated in decimals of a yard or meter, rather than a foot, because of the greater size of the decimals, which makes for easier reading at great distances. Stadia rods are usually from twelve to fifteen feet long, and some are collapsible to permit easy handling.

The ordinary transit has a telescope on which one of the lenses has inscribed four cross hairs, three horizontal and one vertical. These hairs are centered on the lens. The vertical hair is used for lining up taping operations. The middle horizontal hair is used for leveling, which will be discussed later. The top and bottom cross hairs are used for stadia work, with which we are concerned at the present.

The instrumentman, or transitman, in looking through the transit telescope at the stadia rod which is some distance away, will notice that the upper and lower cross hairs will lie at certain points on the rod. The reading between the two hairs multiplied

TESTING WIND VELOCITY AND DIRECTION

The observer using a theodolite reports varying positions of the pilot balloon and reports to the computer at the plotting board in the office.

Courtesy Weather Bureau, U. S. Dept. of Agriculture

by one hundred (for most transits) will tell him how far away the rod is located from the transit. For instance, if the transit-man sees the lower cross hair on the five-foot mark of the rod, and the upper cross hair on the eight-foot mark, he will know that since the difference in readings is three feet, the distance to the rod is three hundred feet. The telescope is mounted on a circular base, so it may be revolved horizontally. This enables the instrumentman to follow the rod to different locations, noting the angle away from a "base line" as well as the distance from the transit.

THE HEIGHT OF THE LAND

It is very often the case during a survey that the party will come across ground of irregular elevation. It then becomes necessary to measure the heights of hills and probably the depths of holes and river beds, etc. If, for example, the distance to a peak is desired, two transits are set up at locations where the distance between can be taped off. This line will then be used as a reference line. Both transits (one on each side of the desired point) will be trained on the peak, with the angles away from the base line noted. A triangle is then formed by the line between transits forming one side, the line from transit number one to the peak forming the second side, and the line from transit number two to the same peak forming the third side. Thus two angles and the length of one side of the triangle are known. The distance from each transit to the peak can be calculated by a trigonometric formula known as the "Law of Sines." The angle of each transit made with the vertical is also known, hence the newly found distance to the peak can be used to compute the horizontal distance to a point directly beneath the peak. So, also, can the vertical elevation of the peak be ascertained. This system is known as "triangulation," which was previously explained and it proves to be an invaluable method in measuring heights and distances of inaccessible locations.

Another way of finding elevations is a method termed "leveling." This is done chiefly in work involving the determination of contours (or elevations above sea level), for the construction of contour maps. Highway and railroad construction requires this method as the basis for laying out designs.

The telescopic instrument used in leveling is called a "level." It consists essentially of a telescope with an attached sensitive bubble tube, such as is found on a carpenter's level for alignment purposes. The rod or "level rod" that is used is similar to the stadia rod that was previously described, in that it is marked in feet and hundredths of a foot. Various manufacturers may have their own special innovations to facilitate rod reading, but in general they are all of a basic fundamental design.

The system of leveling is briefly as follows: The level is set up at a known elevation. (The United States Coast and Geodetic Survey has established points all over the country of known elevation above sea level.) The height of the instrument is then determined, that is, the distance from the ground to the line of sight passing through the telescope. This will not always be constant, because the legs of the tripod may be spread out more at one set-up than

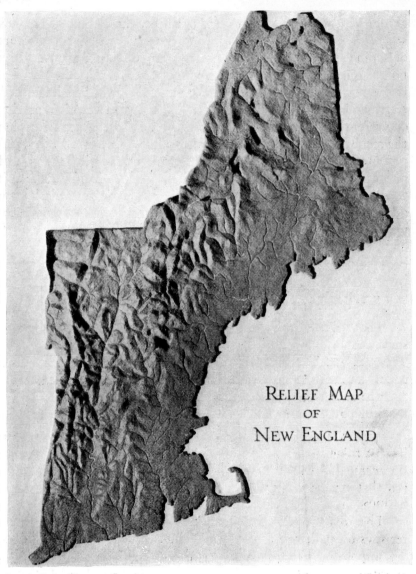

RELIEF MAP
OF
NEW ENGLAND

Courtesy National Resources Committee

RELIEF MAP OF NEW ENGLAND

at another. The instrumentman looks through his level and notes
where the horizontal cross hair falls across the level rod. By means
of simple arithmetic he can determine the elevation at that point.
For example, if the elevation of the ground above sea level is
known to be one hundred fifty feet, and the height of the instrument is found to be five feet, the total height above sea level becomes one hundred fifty-five feet. If the cross hair falls across
the rod at the three-foot mark, it means the ground there is two
feet higher than the ground at the instrument, hence the elevation
is one hundred fifty-two feet at the rod. If comparative heights
are desired for a simple survey and the elevation above sea level is
unknown, an arbitrary quantity may be selected such as one hundred feet, providing no other spots in the vicinity are lower. Neg-
ative values would result if there were lower places, and calculations would become confusing.

TOPOGRAPHY—THE LAY OF THE LAND

The United States Geological Survey has made topographic
surveys and maps of approximately one-half of the United States.
The maps are on a scale of one inch equals one mile and one inch
equals two miles. The process of making these maps is expensive
and the alert engineer will avail himself of these maps rather than
make his own.

Most of the United States has been divided into sections. The
territory that the Federal Government has not sectionized includes
the original Thirteen Colonies, Kentucky, Tennessee, and Texas,
together with government land, such as forest and Indian reser-
vations.

The topographic map depicts on paper the general characteristics of the land that has been mapped. Some actual features
are impossible to reproduce, however, hence symbols have been
adopted to represent them. The most notable example is elevation.
It is not possible to picture actual differences in elevations, so lines
are drawn, each representing a certain elevation. These lines are
called "contour" lines, and they show where an imaginary elevation line would run along the ground. There is, however, one
actual contour line in existence, and this is the shore line of a body

of still water. The water is at a uniform elevation and the line of intersection between it and the shore forms an actual contour line.

Contour lines on a map would run close together when a cliff or steep slope was illustrated and they would be widely spaced over a fairly plane area. These contours and their manner of spacing give the engineer an immediate picture of the type of country he is concerned with, even though he may be many miles from the actual scene.

There are others who have use of the topographic map, and these include the geologist and the military commander. The

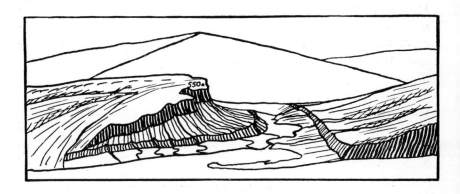

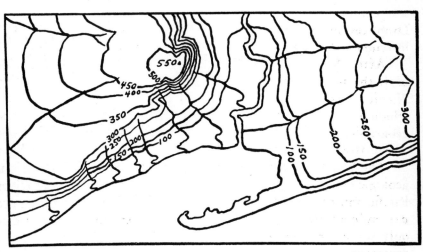

IDEAL SKETCH AND CORRESPONDING TOPOGRAPHICAL CONTOUR MAP

geologist can tell a number of things from such a map. If he is in known oil country, for instance, the location of an untapped source may be determined by hilly regions, or he may be able to get an idea of the strata formations of that particular area.

The military commander, of course, has an urgent need of a topographic map. By its use he can determine the best locations for the offensive or defensive maneuvers of his troops. Sites for camps, communication lines, bridges, roads and other projects are best decided if a map of the territory is first consulted and studied.

The United States Government has made provisions for extensive surveying as mentioned before. The vast regions west of the Mississippi River were the principal territories surveyed. In the strict sense of the word, the earliest governmental explorations could hardly be termed surveys, but maps of a sort were prepared and these provided much information about the little known West.

The Lewis and Clark expedition mapped the country between Lake Superior and the Pacific Coast from the thirty-ninth to the forty-ninth parallel. Major Z. M. Pike's expedition in 1805-1807 explored and mapped the sources of three of the great rivers, the Mississippi, the Arkansas, and the Red Rivers.

The Army made many surveys during the first half of the nineteenth century for military roads. The principal equipment was composed of sextants, pocket chronometer, and compasses. Distances, in the majority of cases, were estimated, but the other instruments afforded a knowledge of direction and location.

After the United States Army Corps of Engineers was organized, the first notable survey under its auspices was that of N. Nicollet, from 1836-1840. The expedition resulted in a map which has been regarded as a most important contribution to geographic knowledge. Nicollet's party explored the basin of the upper Mississippi River, using barometers to determine elevations.

The War Department in 1853 sent army officers together with geologic and topographic assistants to map territories for proposed Pacific railroads. These surveys were not far from the present-day railroad routes to the coast. The expedition furnished not only survey information but also many data on natural history, resources, etc.

Drawing by Raeburn Rohrbach

MAP SHOWING ROUTE OF LEWIS AND CLARK EXPEDITION FROM
ST. LOUIS, MISSOURI, TO OREGON AND RETURN

The latter half of the nineteenth century saw considerable boundary surveying. Various organizations shared in this work; some were appointed commissions, some were various branches of the Army, and some were parties designated by certain territories to do the work. The latter is illustrated in the Louisiana-Texas line survey in 1840. Surveyors appointed by Texas co-operated with army engineers in this particular project.

Of course, this work was not easy. Transportation facilities were not of the best and knowledge of the country was practically negligible. Hardships were suffered by surveying parties of the past, and even by those of the present day who are putting this country on a scale of one inch equals one mile, and one inch equals two miles. There is a great deal to be done yet, but the expeditions of the past have given information that has made possible some of the outstanding progress this country has made since Revolutionary Days.

Another interesting result of these early expeditions was the number of trails they blazed which were later used by the pioneers in their westward journeys, and which are the foundation of some of our most familiar highways and railroads.

NO REASON FOR GETTING LOST

Those of us living in the present day should be extremely thankful for the multitude of maps we have at our disposal. They have made it possible for us to journey to far places with greater ease and security. On land, at sea, and in the air, we are able constantly to keep a check on our position, thereby insuring that we are not off our course, or that we shall not miss our destination.

Today, most of us rely on road maps to guide us from one part of the country to another. This country has become literally a spider web of highways and those of most importance are duly recorded on maps for our guidance. These maps differ from topographic maps in that elevations are not recorded, nor are some of the characteristics of the country. Rivers, however, are depicted along with the towns of the vicinity. The placing of towns does not call for an exact replica of its shape as defined by its boundaries. Frequently the towns and villages are merely denoted by a circle or some such symbol, its relative location on the map being the important thing. It must be remembered, however, that the work of drawing up these maps does not consist of merely drawing a line representing a highway and dropping a dot on it to indicate a town. Very precise topographic maps are drawn as a preliminary step, and from these, the relative positions of highways, towns, rivers, etc., are transferred to a smaller scale, the size of the ordinary present-day road map.

Fine road maps did not always exist and people were not always able to get from one place to another as easily as we do now. Even as recently as a hundred years ago, many of the sites of our great cities were merely open areas of timber and prairie. The early expeditions in traveling from place to place blazed trails that gradually became the routes of many of our great highways. Some of our early railroads also were laid out following the old trails. The Old Santa Fe trail is the foundation of what today is one of our well-known Western railroads. Pathways along many rivers and canals have also become great highways and railroads.

Various methods were used in ancient times to mark or blaze trails. One of the best known was chopping off a bit of bark from trees along the route. These marks were used as a guide on the

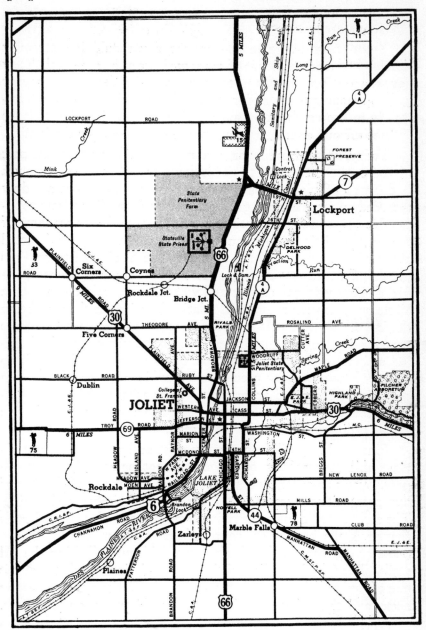

SECTION OF A MODERN HIGHWAY MAP

return journey. Another method was to take notice and become acquainted with unusual or easily remembered features of the country being traveled. After a few trips, the traveler would become well acquainted with these landmarks, as they are called, and the route became very familiar.

Today a surveyor, in order to find his way along, must be able to interpret a topographic map and know just how to go about relocating any point on the ground that he sees depicted on a map. This procedure, of course, involves a little more complicated study and knowledge than merely reaching a point by referring to a road map. The fundamental principle is the same in both cases, picking a starting or reference point and following directions to the destination. In the case of a highway map, we locate the correct road to travel, and after getting on that road we travel it a stated number of miles to the end of our journey. In the case of a topographic map, angles, distances, and elevations are substituted for the highway.

THE GUIDE POSTS OF THE SEA

The art, or science, of finding one's position at sea is called "navigation." There are many types of navigation and some are more refined and complicated than others.

Before the introduction of the compass in about the fourteenth century, the only practical means of determining positions on the sea was to keep in sight of the shore. This, of course, prevented long trips across open bodies of water. Some Eastern waters are an exception. They are affected by monsoon winds which are reasonably consistent in direction. Mariners in these vicinities were able successfully to navigate long stretches by merely running before the wind.

Prior to the eighteenth century, it was possible to find only latitude with the meager instruments available. The only means of determining longitude was by dead reckoning, or estimating the run of the ship. The invention of the chronometer, or time-keeping device, about 1735 made it possible to compute longitude. The value of the instrument, however, was not of definite character until about forty years later.

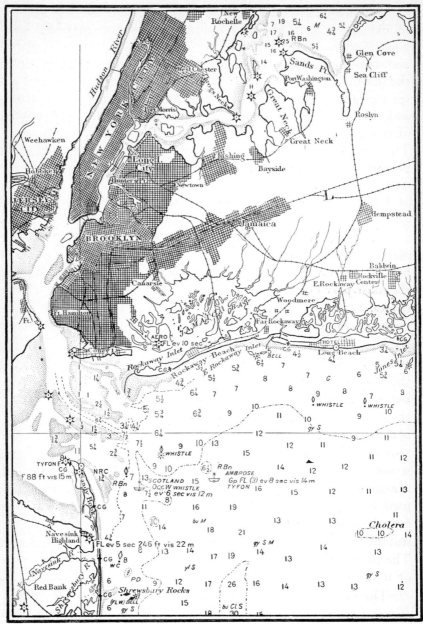

Courtesy U. S. Coast and Geodetic Survey

SECTION OF GOVERNMENT CHART SHOWING APPROACHES TO
NEW YORK HARBOR

The nineteenth century saw rapid strides in the development of navigation instruments as more precision was attained, textbooks and mathematical tables for computation were available, and sounding devices were introduced. These instruments enabled the mariner to determine the depth of the particular place in the sea through which he was sailing. This resulted in many charts and the establishment of good ocean lanes. The progress and art of navigation are still inseparably associated with chart drawing The number and accuracy of these charts have been steadily improved by marine hydrographic and coast survey service. An interesting sidelight in the work of these organizations is the location of fresh water springs in the floor of the ocean off the southeastern coast of the United States.

The size of vessels increased along with progress in the method of steering them. The early Egyptians, however, had boats large enough to be called ships as early as 3000 B.C., but for the most part boats were smaller when navigation permitted only coastal travel. Then, as navigating aids were developed, longer trips became possible, and larger boats were built for these trips.

Sundials were frequently used for daytime travel, and the pole-star was relied upon for direction-finding at night. Although the science of measuring the altitude of heavenly bodies is very old, this system was not used in navigation until voyages beyond the confines of the Mediterranean became common. An instrument called the cross-staff was the first practical instrument employing this system of measuring stars. The date of its invention is not accurately known, but it was mentioned in an edition of *Margarita Philosophica* in 1496, and Columbus was said to have used it on his voyages some years earlier. Its principal use was for the calculation of latitude and, after the preparation of suitable mathematical tables, for the computation of longitude. The principle was a measurement of the distance between a star of fixed position and the moon.

The modern art of navigation requires the use of many precise and accurate instruments and the technique is quite involved and complicated. Higher mathematics and the physics of light play most important roles.

Simpler forms of modern navigation include piloting in and out of ports, keeping the ship in channels by means of beacons, buoys, landmarks, ranges, and lighthouses. Pilots are in charge of merchant service ships in port vicinities, but do not handle naval vessels, except in extreme cases where special conditions require the knowledge and experience of a local pilot. After a ship leaves the harbor and reaches open sea, the pilot is "dropped," or lowered to a smaller boat which returns him to port. The big ship then determines its position by compass bearings or other means and proceeds on its way.

NAVIGATION WAS A PERILOUS AFFAIR WHEN THESE SHIPS
WERE CALLED "MODERN"

THE ENGINEERING OF MINING

AMONG THE CHIEF BUILDING BLOCKS of all civilizations are the metals. They even give names to key stages in the development of mankind: the golden age, the bronze age, the iron age. Today might be called variously the steel age, the age of alloys, or the age of all metals. Metals make possible not only the instruments of warfare, but also the more important instruments of peace: machines and scientific devices, printing presses and plows, the necessities and conveniences of modern life. Nor are the metals the only substances that must be dangerously won from under the hard crust of earth: coal and petroleum, salt and sulphur, illuminating gas and helium—to name only a few—are of equal importance.

Even as mining is essential to a civilization built upon industry, so the engineer is essential to mining. His task is always a difficult one. The man who lays out cities and roads can take advantage of the topography of the land. It is different with the mining engineer; topography takes advantage of *him!* He has to follow the devious underground channelings of ore-bearing veins and offshoots, and they often lead him a merry chase. Except for coal and petroleum, few valuable minerals are found in convenient localized chunks or definite strata. Most of them were deposited by the seeping and trickling of the underground waters in past ages. The intricate pattern of this seepage may be further confused by shifts and earthquakes. The engineer's detective-like task of following the twistings and breaks of the pattern is additionally complicated by questions of economy. Except for occasional breathtaking clusters of gold nuggets and streaks of concentrated "pay dirt," most ores are so mixed with waste matter that only the most laborious and thrifty methods of mining and refining will yield a profit. Certain Alaskan gold mines have been successfully worked despite the fact that only two dollars' worth of metal was obtained from every ton of original material. A

Courtesy Buffalo Museum of Science

MODEL SHOWING PRIMITIVE MINING OF IRON ORE

slight drop in the price of metals may compel such mines to stop operations. The discovery of a better refining process may put them back in business again. The engineer cannot drive tunnels or dig pits wholesale. Before he puts any new plan into operation, he has to answer the question: "Is it worth it?"

DRAINING THE COMSTOCK LODE

In addition, the mining engineer must continually face and overcome all sorts of unexpected hindrances and sudden emergencies. Let us take a case from the last century. In 1859 the famous Comstock lode, a large deposit of silver, was discovered in Nevada. Shafts were sunk down into the hillside and horizontal galleries driven out from them to tap the lode. However, within a few years one of the many natural enemies of miners appeared from out of the earth—water. It flooded the lower levels of the mines to such an extent that operations there became unprofitable; the cost of pumping was too high. It was then proposed to

Courtesy Buffalo Museum of Science

PRIMITIVE IRON FABRICATING OPERATIONS

dig a horizontal tunnel that could be used as a drain, a tunnel that would start in lower ground four miles away and reach an eventual depth of two thousand feet. The blasting and excavating of this tunnel was commenced in 1871 and was not finished for seven years. Hand drills were used at first, then drills run by compressed air. Every foot won into the hillside had to be carefully shored and timbered to prevent a collapsing of the treacherous earth. As in the lode itself, water was a dangerous enemy; it threatened to choke off the passageway by swelling the clay through which it was cut. Mule trains served to drag out the excavated earth. Ventilation shafts were sunk from above, but eventually the tunnel reached such a depth that they became impractical. Without ventilation, however, the air became so foul and the temperature rose to such an extent that work was impossible. A resourceful engineer cut a series of small holes in the tubes that supplied the drills with compressed air from outside, so constructing a rude but efficient ventilation system. Eventually they broke through to the shafts in the Comstock lode. Those

Courtesy Bureau of M nes, U. S. Dept. of Interior

CAGE ENTRANCE TO AN IRON MINE

seven spectacular years of work, dogged yet ingenious, rough-and-ready yet scientific, are not so much exceptional as they are characteristic of the daily activity of mining engineers. Speed is almost always a prime consideration; each loss of time is a money loss. Yet seven-year jobs are by no means unusual. Half a dozen such pieces of work may make up an engineer's whole career. He does not have an easy time building miner's workshops deep under the earth.

PROSPECTING

Few characters have such an aura of romance as the old-time prospector of the California gold rush. Books and moving pictures delight in depicting him wandering off down the trail with his blanket, frying pan, donkey, pick, and shovel, tapping at outcroppings of rock, miraculously discovering nuggets in a dry stream bed. Such men did occasionally find gold, but the writers of romances both magnify their individual ability and underestimate the difficulty of their job.

Courtesy Oliver Iron Mining Co.

PROTECTIVE TIMBERING AFTER BLASTING

PANNING GOLD
FROM AN ALAS-
KAN STREAM

Courtesy
The Alaska Railroad
Photo by Rolphe Dauphin

Before ores can be mined, they must be found, and the finding is not an easy task. As we have shown before, most ores are deposited in porous rock by the devious seepage of underground waters. Sometimes, notably in the cases of mercury and antimony, these waters are hot, being forced upward from underground volcanic sources rich in certain minerals. More often they are ordinary ground waters, having their origin in rain and streams and lakes.

Long after such veins of minerals are deposited, wind and surface water may cut down to them through the earth and expose them. A swift stream may gouge a deep gorge down to a vein and then wear its way right through the vein, eroding the ores and carrying them downstream, in the form of a gravel or fine powder. In the case of gold or platinum or tin, the pure metal itself may be so carried, rather than one of its chemical compounds. Being heavy, such metals will begin to sink to the bottom at the first place where the water eddies or slows up. So the old western prospector could follow the streams, keeping his eyes peeled for sandbars, bends, shallows, and pools. At each likely spot he would examine the sand for traces of pay dirt. Such a "placer" deposit might not be very valuable in itself but, in any case, it carried the information that a mother lode would very likely be discovered somewhere upstream.

The number of ores that make such placer deposits are limited. However, gorges, ravines, and mountainsides are always favorable ground for the prospector, since many strata are laid open to view in cross-section. Yet, even his quest is a difficult one. He must be able to recognize the ores, sometimes by the characteristic color that weathering gives them; he must be able to tell the true from the false, real gold from glittering iron pyrite, "fool's gold." But if he is in a country of few rock outcroppings, of much surface dirt and vegetation, his difficulties are multiplied tenfold. Here a sound knowledge of geology becomes very useful, enabling the prospector to get a general picture of the levels of dirt and rock in the terrain, and gauge the possibilities of each level by a few tests. His work becomes a little less hit-and-miss; he sees the country in which he operates as an organized whole.

Courtesy Canadian National Railways

GOLD MINE AT JUNEAU, ALASKA

SCIENTIFIC DIVINING RODS

Today science has come even more to the prospector's aid and puts into his hands instruments that spy down into the solid earth. For example, the magnetic needle helps him in his search for iron ore. The compass needle not only points north; it also has a tendency to point downward, a tendency that becomes greater the farther north or south a person goes. The normal angle of this dip is known for each part of the earth. Therefore, if the prospector notices that his needle is dipping more than would be normally expected, he knows that there is a body of iron ore under his feet, its magnetic field interfering with that of the earth. The ancients believed, and the superstition still remains, that "divining rods" made of certain woods would tend to dip down when carried over a deposit of ore by a person of supernatural ability. By coincidence the modern magnetic iron divining rod happens to act in just the same way! However, its use is limited to the search for iron ore.

The electric current widens the field of investigation. Certain ores, especially when sulphur is one of their chemical constituents, tend to dissolve in underground water, so making it a better conductor and setting up a natural battery or wet-cell under the surface of the earth, currents flowing from rocks of higher potential to rocks of lower potential. Two copper rods, stuck down into the earth and connected to a galvanometer will contact this current. The galvanometer measures this current and gives the prospector a rough idea of whether or not there is a sizable amount of ore beneath his feet.

This method can only be used where the ground is wet. Where the ground is dry or the ores are not of such a nature as to make a natural wet-cell, the prospector can bring the radio to his aid. Radio waves are sent down and excite bodies of ore, which develop a secondary field. This secondary field is investigated by a receiving set. The prospector tunes in on the metals! By moving his receiving set around he is able to judge the extent and location of the bodies of ore. By comparing the angle at which the primary waves go down with the angle at which the secondary waves come up, he is able to determine the depth of the subterranean minerals. In short, he is surveying the invisible depths of earth by means of radio.

EARTHQUAKES TO FIND SALT

But even when the resources of the magnetic field, electric current, and radio wave are exhausted, the scientific prospector does not rest. He enlists into his service earthquakes and gravity. First, let us consider gravity. For every point of the earth's surface the normal force of gravitational attraction is known. Delicate torsion balances can measure slight deviations from this normal force, deviations caused by the presence of abnormally heavy or light masses under the earth. These masses may turn out to be valuable minerals. When, on the other hand, an earthquake occurs, compression of waves starts through the interior of the earth

Photo by Robert Yarnell Richie

A WORKER IN A SALT MILL

Courtesy Bureau of Mines, U. S. Dept. of Interior

MILL OF A LOUISIANA SALT COMPANY

in straight lines, and so are the first waves to be picked up by distant seismographic stations. These compressional waves vary in
speed along the way, moving more swiftly through materials of
low density and high elasticity. Salt is such a material, and there
happen to be large deposits of salt around the gulf of Mexico.
The deposits are in the form of great domes buried a few thousand feet under the earth. Now this salt is too deep to be profitably mined, but experience has shown that there is almost always
a deposit of sulphur or a pool of petroleum at the top of each
dome. In other words, the salt is the clue to the more valuable
treasure. It speeds up compressional waves, and this speeding up
can be discovered.

However, the prospector cannot make use of the waves from
actual earthquakes. First, it would be difficult to determine the
precise time at which they started; second, he might have to wait
a long time for one to come from the right direction; third, distant bodies other than salt domes might have an effect on the speed

of the wave. Therefore, he makes little earthquakes of his own. Charges of explosives are buried about twenty feet down in the earth in the center of the critical locality. Seismographs, placed round in a distant circle, record the exact time of the coming of the compressional waves, and are informed by radio of the exact time of the explosion. From these data the speed of the wave can be calculated. When a salt dome is in the line between the explosion and one of the seismographs, the compressional wave gets to that station before it gets to the others. A second explosion set off at a different place will locate another straight line passing through the same dome. Drilling at the point of intersection of the two lines will tap the valuable sulphur or petroleum.

UNDERGROUND PROSPECTING

The impressive list of the modern scientific instruments used in seeking minerals tends to give one the idea that prospecting has become a cut and dried process. This is by no means so. The instruments themselves are often very costly and always very tricky; only under the most careful handling will they give dependable results, and those results are difficult to interpret. Certain minerals evade all instruments and certain localities are unsuited to their use. Today, as in the past, many deposits of ore are still found by a mixture of luck and persistence. Luck played a chief part in the discoveries that started the gold rushes to California, Alaska, and Australia, and it continues to do so. In any case, when the approximate position and depth of an ore body are determined, holes must be drilled down to check that determination, discover the exact nature of the ore, and decide whether it is of sufficient concentration to make mining and refining profitable.

At first sight the problem of sinking a small hole deep into the earth seems easy. However, a little reflection shows that it is fraught with all sorts of difficulties. How are the sides to be kept from caving in? How is the loose earth or rock to be removed, especially when the hole is no more than a few inches in diameter? How can an auger or drill be effectively operated when the hole

SHAFT OF IRON MINE,
SHOWING SKIPS AND
CAGES

Courtesy Bureau of Mines,
U. S. Dept. of Interior

becomes several hundred feet deep? What is to be done when
alternate levels of hard rock, soft rock, sand, and earth have to
be penetrated? The man who digs shallow holes for fence posts
has no easy time. The prospector who sinks deep borings has a
very hard one.

To begin with the simpler solutions of the problem, consider
the search for placer deposits of gold. These placers are sometimes
found a few inches below the surface of a stream bed, but more
often they are covered over with many feet of sand, gravel, and
loose dirt. To penetrate this alluvial rubbish it is possible to use
augers of the same sort as are used for post holes. The head consists
of a sharp bladed spiral of metal that cuts or planes its way into the
ground like a brace and bit. The handle consists of a metal rod or
pipe, made up in sections about five feet long. A cross-bar is

attached to the top of the handle; by means of it, one or two men can rotate the head of the auger and screw it down into the earth. Every once in a while they pull out the auger and remove the dirt that is lodged between its spirals; in this way they both keep the hole clear and also get the samples they are after. When they have driven the boring five feet deep, they fit on another section of handle, attach the cross-bar to its top, and continue their work. If they encounter a section of ground that tends to cave in, they force down sections of stove pipe casing to line the hole.

When these hand augers arrive at a depth of sixty or seventy feet, their limitations are obvious. The longer the jointed handle becomes the more it tends to twist along its length, and the more strength is required to oppose this twist and also turn the auger head. It becomes more and more difficult to drive down the casing and more and more arduous to draw up the head, clear the hole, and take samples. To overcome these obstacles many other kinds of drill have been devised. In some the casing itself is provided with a cutting edge and is rotated by horsepower and so driven down along with the interior drill. But others employ radically new arrangements.

Courtesy Hudson Coal Company

DRILLING FOR A BLAST IN AN ANTHRACITE MINE

Courtesy Bureau of Mines, U. S. Dept. of Interior

DRILLING BLAST HOLES IN SOLIDIFIED SULPHUR

CHURNS AND BLACK DIAMONDS

The old principle of the butter churn is used by the so-called rope drill. A spiked or chisel-like drill weighing from five hundred to fifteen hundred pounds is let down into the boring on a rope, and then alternately hoisted and dropped by means of an engine and derrick crashing its way down through earth and rock. The material it crushes and softens is sucked up into a vacuum pump that is attached to a separate rope; when the pump is filled it is hoisted and emptied. The casing for the boring is made in jointed stove-pipe-like sections that are driven in one on top of the other; when the one at the surface is driven down the one at the bottom is thereby pushed farther into the earth, so keeping pace with the drill and the vacuum pump. But by what force is this casing driven down? The engineers have a simple yet exceedingly ingenious solution for this problem. They pull up the heavy drill a short distance, clamp the rope that holds it to the top section of casing, then start hoisting and dropping the drill. The drill has not enough rope to enable it to hit bottom; therefore, the force of its fall is expended in jerking down the rope and so yanking the casing farther and farther into the earth! By a use of the churning arrangement a depth of three thousand feet can be attained.

Even greater depths are reached by the diamond drill, which uses the hardest of gems to win its way through the hardest rock. The drill head is fixed at the bottom of a set of metal rods. These rods are spun by a small engine at the surface. Through their hollow core, water is forced down under pressure; this water returns to the surface *outside* the rod, carrying with it the waste material and so keeping the boring clean. The drill head itself consists of a ring of soft steel, its under-surface set with six or more black diamonds, gems even tougher than the sparkling transparent stone of commerce and adornment.

Appropriately enough, this instrument is especially used in the South African gold fields, diamonds from nearby Kimberley serving to explore the deep veins of yellow metal in the Transvaal. Unlike the hand auger and churn, it is a drill that depends upon rapidity of spin rather than brute force, eating its way into hard rock at a speed of from two to three feet an hour. Since it is mounted on rigid rods it can be driven into the earth at any angle, even vertically upward. Yet even this cunning instrument is most difficult and exasperating to use. When softer rock is encountered, the drill head must be changed to one of steel for fear that the precious gems will be torn out and lost. The rods tend to bend as they are pushed downward, and so to change the direction of the boring from a straight line to a curve. Often the whole head breaks off and is lost; it has to be drawn up every few feet and examined. Truly, and despite all ingenious devices, there is no easy way of boring holes into the earth.

GETTING GOLD FROM PAY DIRT

As soon as a sufficient number of samples have assured the prospector that the ore deposit is rich enough to warrant mining and refining, a bigger task falls to the lot of the engineer. Minerals must be brought to the surface in large quantities. Pits must

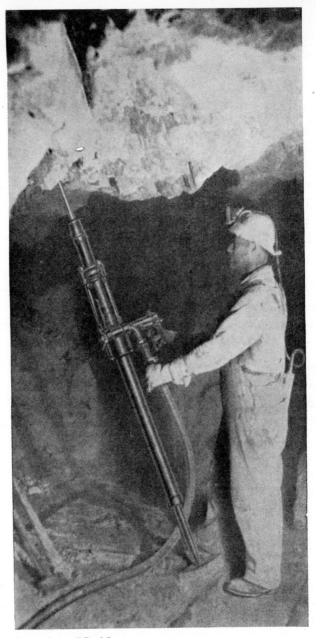

Courtesy Ingersoll-Rand Co.

A DRY ROCK DRILL IN A NORTHERN MINE

be dug or shafts must be sunk. Men must go down into the earth. The engineer not only has to plan and supervise the digging of the pits and shafts; he must also make them as safe as possible for the men that use them. His tunnels must be built in such a way as to minimize the inescapable dangers of collapse, fire, water, explosion, and poisonous gases.

However, before considering the deeper delvings of the engineer, let us turn our attention to the methods whereby the gold seekers filled their leather bags with precious dust and nuggets. The men who fought cold and hunger in the Yukon found their gold mixed with tons of gravel and fine sand. This pay dirt could not profitably be transported away from its source. The metal had to be extracted on the spot. The simplest method was panning. The pay dirt was mixed with water in a box set on rockers. When this box was joggled and shaken from side to side, the heavy gold would settle to the bottom, while the dirt itself would slosh out over the sides with the water. Slowly more pay dirt and water were added; slowly the gold accumulated at the bottom, until there was a precious baby in the "cradle."

But panning was a slow and primitive process at best. Work on a much larger scale could be accomplished by sluicing. A flat-bottomed wooden trough several hundred feet long was built and slanted at a slight angle. A slush of pay dirt and water was then fed in at the upper end and allowed to flow through. Along the bottom of the trough were placed a number of short poles or crosswise bars called riffles; these helped to retain the gold when it sank, preventing it from sliding along the bottom. Sometimes mercury was put in with the riffles; it would catch truant gold by forming an amalgam with it. Later the two metals could be separated.

In these ways the men who braved the Yukon won their fortunes. Sluicing is a process that is still in use. The main difficulty is that of getting the pay dirt and water to the top of the sluice. Sometimes shovels and wheelbarrows are used, sometimes steam shovels, sometimes dragline excavators—great toothed spoons that are pulled about by a cable and so scrape up the surface gravel and sand. Today powerful hoses are often employed, hydraulic

AIR MOTOR DRIV-
EN DIAMOND
CORE DRILL

Courtesy
Ingersoll-Rand Co.

"giants" that bombard the pay dirt with mighty jets of water, loosening it and washing it into the head of the trough, even as a gardener washes gravel out of a lawn.

PITS AND GLORY HOLES

If a vein of precious mineral extends to the surface of the earth, its upper portions can often be mined directly in much the same fashion as rocks are quarried. When men go after shallow

deposits of iron ore in Minnesota or of copper in the southwestern
states, they may begin by using a plow dragged by a horse or
tractor. They are preparing not to sow but to reap! A scraper
will follow the plow, removing the material that has been loosened, and carrying it to waste dumps. When the ore is reached,
a line of vertical holes is bored into it near one of its outer edges.
Explosives are put into these and touched off by means of fuses or
electric sparks. A section of ore crumbles off and falls to one side;
if the amount of the explosive and the position of the holes have
been properly calculated by the engineer, the resulting fragments
will be small enough to be easily handled by the shovels that feed
the wagons or cars. When they have been loaded, another line of
explosives will be placed and fired, another heaped line of ore
fragments produced and shoveled away. These operations will be
repeated until a whole level or slice has been blasted from the
top of the body of ore. Then scrapers or steam shovels will set
about to clear away more dirt and waste, so exposing the next
section of ore to be blasted out. The great hole grows in depth,
and the work proceeds. The engineer must carefully calculate the
slant of the sides of the deepening pit. If they are too steep, there

PREPARATIONS
FOR FIRING A
BLAST IN A
HOLE DRILLED
INTO A SUL-
PHUR BED

Courtesy
Bureau of Mines,
U. S. Dept. of Interior

Courtesy Hibbing Tourist & Information Bureau
PRESENT-DAY MONSTER OF IRON AND STEEL
A 300-ton shovel loading iron ore into railroad cars for shipment to the
docks at Duluth.

is danger of their breaking away and sliding down, delaying work,
burying machinery, and injuring workmen. If they are made un-
necessarily shallow, their excavation will cost too much money,
and profits will vanish.

The plow and scraper are among the simplest devices employed in open-pit mining. Dipper dredges, hydraulic excavators,
boom derricks, and locomotive cranes: all these may be used to
gouge into the earth. A continuous chain of buckets may dip
down from out of the heart of a great machine, bite viciously
into the blasted fragments, come up filled, and then empty their
contents into a car. Or a steam shovel may be placed in the bottom of the pit. The stiff arm of its boom will drive a titan shovel
down and scoop up several cubic yards of broken ore, raise them
to the edge of the pit, and dump them out. Perhaps a ramp will
spiral down into the pit; on it will be laid narrow-gage railroad
track in order that little cars may pursue the steam shovel down
and take the ore it wins to the surface. The work proceeds swiftly;
different operations are carried on simultaneously. The engineer
must be watching and calculating all the time, checking, plan-

ning, advising, conserving. Yet, no matter how well he does his work, there comes a time when open-pit mining becomes unprofitable. The deeper the hole is dug, the wider its sides must be; eventually the expenses eat up the profits and some other method must be used.

The most obvious alternative is the glory hole, a somewhat unrespectable brother of the open-pit scheme. A shaft is sunk straight down into the earth and a horizontal tunnel dug from its bottom into the core of the body of ore. Here it intersects another shaft or "glory hole" leading to the surface. Charges of explosive are set off in the wall of this second shaft; the rock is loosened, tumbles down, and is dragged off through the tunnel and hoisted to the surface through the first shaft. Then another series of charges is placed and exploded; slowly the glory hole is enlarged and the ore won. However, this method is exceedingly dangerous. Blasts may block the horizontal tunnel or cause it to collapse. Partly loosened rocks may not fall until some time after the explosion; then they may hurtle down on the heads of the

TRANSPORTING COAL IN A MINE

Courtesy Hibbing Tourist & Information Bureau
MILLING OPERATIONS AT A COMBINATION UNDERGROUND-
OPEN-PIT MINE

Courtesy Hibbing Tourist & Information Bureau
MOVING TEMPORARY TRACKS IN AN OPEN-PIT IRON MINE

workers who are engaged in loading the cars that run through the tunnel. It is a makeshift scheme at best. When engineers build in earth and solid rock, they must build soundly.

UNDERGROUND WORKSHOPS

Imagine a skyscraper built, not up into the air, but down into the ground. Imagine it nonetheless equipped with elevators, with an air-conditioning system, with electric lights, and pipes for water and sewage. Finally, imagine it going deeper into the ground than any skyscraper rises into the air. Then you will have a general idea of what those mines are like that delve after seams of coal, veins of copper ore, deposits of tin, silver, and gold.

The main elevator shaft is the chief artery of the mine. Through it the workmen descend to their labors; from it they emerge at the end of a shift, grimed and tired, to make their way to the changing rooms where they put off their dusty garments. Through it powerful fans drive the fresh air down to the depths or suck up the foul. Up it is hoisted the ore that has been blasted and broken out. At its bottom is the sump, a cavity in which the ground water collects. Along its length run pipes to pump out that water and prevent flooding.

The various levels of the mine correspond generally to the floors of the skyscraper but there are many important differences. The levels are much farther apart; in other words, there is much more solid rock than open space in the mine; if this were not so, general collapses and terrible cave-ins would occur. For the same reason, the levels are not open floors but sets of tunnels; whenever a wide room is opened up it must be filled with supports and props. These supports often consist of the natural rock or the ore that is being mined; sometimes wooden ones are used. In general, the mining engineer must make use of the material he finds under the earth. Even as topography dictates to him where he shall drive his tunnels and shafts, so it leaves him little choice as to the means of their construction. The man who builds a skyscraper can think in terms of steel and reinforced concrete; he can weigh the subtle differences between brick and stone; he can employ any particular quality of structural steel he chooses, any

Courtesy Bureau of Mines, U. S. Dept. of Interior
"GOING DOWN!"
Double car coal mine cage equipped with safety catch and manually
operated shaft gates.

one of the many powerful alloys that the metallurgists have devised in their laboratories; there is no end to the number of natural
woods he may employ, the myriads of plastic substances and artificial materials he may use for interior linings and decorative purposes. Finally, he can calculate the strength of every single
element that goes into the structure he is building, he can depend
upon each one to do its part. In comparison the mining engineer
is struggling in the midst of chaos. He can never be sure that the
materials between his shafts and tunnels are sound and solid; there
may be dangerous faults and breaks in the rock strata he is counting on to bastion and support his workings; there may be gaps
and cracks and caves in the very places that he is counting upon
for firm foundations. Borings may suddenly open up a vein of
loose earth or water-swollen clay; his miners may strike upon
water itself and be forced back, all the lower levels endangered.
At every point the engineer must be ready to throw up mighty
props and dams. At every moment he must be prepared to revise
his plans, to change the direction of a tunnel, to abandon one tunnel completely and start work on another. He seeks to build in

solid rock but at any time he may find that he is building in sand.

However, this is only the beginning of his difficulties. The horizontal tunnels that are driven out from the shaft often do not bore their way directly into the minerals that are being sought. Veins of ore or seams of coal are not so obliging; they slant through the earth at steep angles, sometimes they are almost vertically tilted up toward the surface; they are a part of the ages-old crust of earth, twisted by earthquakes, folded and broken by the same forces that made mountains. The horizontal tunnels and the veins of ore are like two sets of parallel lines, the one cutting across the other. At the points where they intersect the profitable work begins. Excavations are driven from there up into the veins themselves. Miners working on platforms or keeping their footing on angled surfaces chip and blast. The fragments of ore they win are let down into the horizontal tunnels. There they are loaded on little cars that run on tracks and so take their burden to the elevator shaft. These cars are operated by electric motors or compressed air, or perhaps hauled by horses or mules that seldom see daylight. Back and forth they shuttle, bearing the raw material that makes an industrial civilization possible.

Courtesy Hudson Coal Company

MULE BARNS IN A COAL MINE
The barns are electrically lighted and well ventilated.

AT THE WORKING FACE

The purpose for the sake of which the engineer plans his skyscraper under the earth, is accomplished at that place where profitable ore is being won, at the "working face" of the rock. Here the miners do their most dangerous and essential work. Picks and bars are called into play. Perhaps a large, half-split chunk must be detached from the ceiling; then the miner will insert a long wedge-ended lever into the split and force the chunk down, the length of the lever minimizing his chances of getting brained in the process. Coal is generally broken out by such methods of wedging. Suppose that the under part of the working face has been cut away and that it is desired to bring down the upper mass. Holes are driven in close to the roof by "power picks," pointed steel bars whose rapid punches are the result of the power of compressed air. Then wedges are driven into the holes and the upper mass comes tumbling down. In place of wedges an ingenious hydraulic cartridge is sometimes used. This

Courtesy Philadelphia & Reading Coal & Iron Co.

MECHANICAL CAR LOADER IN AN ANTHRACITE MINE

consists of a hollow, watertight steel cylinder, narrow enough to fit into the hole made by the power pick. Mounted along the sides of this cylinder are several short plungers. When the cylinder is being inserted these are flush with its outer surface. However, when water under pressure is then pumped into the instrument, they are forced out like so many diminutive hydraulic jacks, and so split the rock.

However, most ores will not yield to such relatively gentle methods. They must be blasted out. Explosions give the engineer another reason to worry about a structure of which he is none too sure in the first place. Holes are drilled into the working face of the ore and charges inserted. These charges may consist of grains of black powder as large as billiard balls or as small as fine shot; they may consist of any of a number of kinds of dynamite. Explosives are very peculiar substances; each has a personality of its own. Some are quick in their action, some are slow. Some are easy to ignite, some are difficult. The dynamites have a great disruptive power; they tend to break rock into tiny fragments. They cannot be easily detonated by flame or spark; a blasting cap has to be used for the purpose, a tiny cylinder of copper containing fulminate of mercury. These caps are treacherous little things and demand much more careful handling than the main explosive; they must not be joggled, they must not be scraped or twisted as they are being inserted into the blasting hole. Black powder, on the other hand, has a greater propulsive than disruptive force; it tends to smash out the rock in large chunks rather than small fragments. It can be set off by a fuse or electric squib.

If the engineer had only to consider the disruptive and propulsive forces of various explosives, he would not have an easy time choosing the best ones for his particular purposes. But that is not all. Explosions are never complete in practice; the various gases they generate are not wholly burnt and some of them are poisonous and some explosive in themselves. The fumes that result from the detonation of most dynamites can be ignited by any chance spark; this is not true of the gelatin variety and therefore it is used extensively. Furthermore, all explosions tend to generate such lethal gases as carbon monoxide and hydrogen sulphide. The

Paul's Photos, Chicago
MINING STILL A HAZARDOUS ENTERPRISE
Despite the best safeguards engineering science can devise, accidents will
occur. Picture shows rescue workers at the scene of a great German mine
disaster in which 248 lives were lost.

engineer must try to keep these at a minimum by selecting the
most suitable powders and dynamites. But, more than that, he
must see that all factors of danger are cut down as much as
possible.

MAKING MINES SAFE

Explosions are by no means the sole source of harmful gases
in the mine. Coal contains a certain amount of marsh gas, which
is liberated during the process of blasting and breaking up. The
very dust of the coal, floating through the narrow passages of the
mine, may form a deadly cloud that the first open flame can set
off, spreading destruction through whole corridors. Candles and
lamps, burning in stuffy air, may produce anhydride. The splitting of certain rocks may liberate explosive hydrogen. A few
of these gases, such as hydrogen sulphide, make themselves known
by their odor. Careful testing is needed to reveal the others.
Caged canaries and mice, because of their extreme sensitivity, serve
to warn against carbon monoxide. The miner must always be
alert. If he carries a lamp, it must be of a safety type. However,
most of all, the engineer must provide thorough and constant

ventilation. A fan located at one surface opening drives fresh air down; it is sucked out at another, thus insuring that it will pass through the horizontal corridors. The mine must be planned in such a way that the ventilation will be complete; there should be no long blind alleys in which air can stagnate. Besides providing adequate ventilation, the engineer is responsible for illumination and drainage; a mine well illuminated and kept free from water is thereby the more safe. Explosion doors and fire doors, fire-fighting apparatus and oxygen helmets, first aid squads and escape shafts that provide the mine with "back doors"—all these must be ready in case of the emergencies of fire and cave-in.

THE INDUSTRY AND THE ENGINEER

The world produces about three billion tons of mining products every year; to this total the United States contributes about one billion. Millions of workmen are employed by the industry. Except in wartimes, more explosives are used to blast rock than for any other purpose. The railroads carry more mineral products

Courtesy Bureau of Mines, Ottawa, Canada

TRAIL SMELTER, TRAIL, B. C.

than they do any other freight. Truly, the industry that produces the metallic building blocks of commercial civilization stands like a giant upon the face of the earth, his feet planted deep in mines and pits and quarries. Around him tower the blazing smelters, the great refineries. He is so big that he dwarfs the many engineers who serve him, giving of their cunning and knowledge and courage that he may grow bigger still.

These engineers are the brains of the business. They make profits grow by eliminating waste and devising new economies. From the working face of the rock to the tunnel below, from the shuttling tunnel cars to the elevators and hoists, they are on the watch for shortcuts, improvements, and safety devices. Their buildings under the earth are of the most difficult sort to construct. Their materials are not of their own choosing. Their tunnels must be arranged to fit the whims of an ore vein. Their work is a continual exploration, from the first boring sent down for samples to the last load of ore taken out of an ancient mine. Prospectors, surveyors, builders, explorers—mining engineers must be all of these to serve their giant industry.

AIR MOTOR OPER-
ATING A VENTI-
LATING FAN IN A
MINE

Courtesy Ingersoll-Rand
Company

THE ENGINEERING OF
TRANSPORTATION

F EW PEOPLE who look at the trade routes of the seas, or the rail, and highway routes as they are depicted on maps, realize that they represent the arteries that carry the life-blood of our civilization. Every line represents a highway on which are carried men and goods from one place to another. They make possible our very life. Each highway, too, represents an engineering feat. Even on the sea and in the air where highways are found ready for man's use, special problems arise if they are to be used: shallows and shoals hamper the unwary mariner, and mountains and high towers are obstacles for flyers. Ports for boats and landing places for airplanes must be prepared. On land, there are even greater problems. No natural rails exist that can be used by trains; likewise, few natural roads that can be used by modern automobiles. On the other hand, there are natural obstacles to every form of movement—these are the problems of the engineer. His is the task of removing obstacles to free and unhampered movement on land and sea, and improving the natural advantages which exist.

THE CONQUEST OF THE SEA

Conquest of the ocean depended first upon building ships that could withstand the buffeting of storms. Navigation instruments had to be devised which would enable seamen to find their remote destinations and to avoid the natural dangers which threatened them with destruction. Ships were made more manageable with the addition of sails and rudders, and through improvements in design. The open seas were comparatively safe for a sturdy vessel in the hands of an experienced crew, but bringing the ship into harbor required an additional, sometimes extraordinary amount of skill.

Homer Smith photo, Chicago

FINANCIAL DISTRICT OF NEW YORK AND EAST RIVER PIERS

Coasts that nature pierced with numerous rivers and indented with bays, invited visits from commercial ships. The eastern coast of the United States has many fine harbors which required only a moderate amount of improvement by engineers. New York has one of the best natural harbors in the world. Other coastal indentations, like the harbors at Rio de Janeiro and San Francisco, with narrow entrances and spacious bays form welcome havens for the sea-buffeted ships. Cape Cod is one of the finest of natural breakwaters. But where such natural advantages do not exist, engineering works must be constructed to protect entrances and prevent storms on the ocean from destroying ships lying at anchor.

Harbors can be made by building breakwaters and by dredging channels through shallow water. The necessity for such projects may be appreciated when it is realized that stormy seas often toss their waves to heights of thirty feet or more. These tremendous waves may exert pressures of more than 6,000 pounds per square foot, and challenge the greatest skill of marine engineers. The outstanding example of the artificial creation of a harbor is that of Buffalo, New York, on Lake Erie. There were

Homer Smith photo, Chicago

SKYLINE OF NEW YORK FROM WEEHAWKEN, N. J.

practically no natural advantages available. Prior to 1903, Buffalo possessed two breakwaters totaling about 10,000 feet in length. Subsequent additions were made until these artificial barriers reached an extent of about four miles. Buffalo, with its man-made harbor, ranks tenth among the ports of the world in tonnage handled annually.

CANALS AND STREAMS

In much the same manner that oceans provide water travel, we also have extensive inland water travel. Aside from the five Great Lakes of the United States, the chief method is river and canal shipping. Rivers are considered natural waterways and canals are treated as either partially or wholly artificial. In other words, a canal is an inland waterway that has been improved or completely designed to provide certain desired facilities. Their size varies from those built to accommodate small craft to deep ship canals such as the Panama and Suez Canals. Although they are not strictly inland waterways they are used to transport water craft over a stretch of land.

Courtesy Buffalo Chamber of Commerce   Photo by Washburn
PEACE BRIDGE AT BUFFALO, NEW YORK
Buffalo is in right foreground, and the Canadian shore in left background.

Very often, a stream will be navigable only in stretches, the remainder being composed of treacherous rapids and waterfalls. Before the introduction of canals, it was necessary to resort to methods of portage to get from one navigable stretch of a river to the next. Portages were also necessary to get from one body of water to another. An example of this is found in the Chicago area, where pioneers were required to trek some ten or twelve miles to get from the foot of Lake Michigan to the Des Plaines River that they might continue their journey down to the Mississippi River. Even before Chicago became organized, the federal government recognized the value of a canal in the vicinity. The result was the Illinois-Michigan Canal that extends from the South Branch of the Chicago River to the Illinois River.

Isthmian and peninsular canals, such as the Panama and Suez, are for the purpose of connecting two bodies of water that are separated by a narrow neck of land.

THE LOCKS

In the case of encircling a falls, it is obvious that the difference in elevation must be dealt with. This is accomplished by "locks," which are chambers to raise or lower a boat from one elevation to another. A chamber consists of gates at either end and artificial sidewalls. If a boat enters a lock at the lower level, water is pumped into the lock, after all gates are closed, until it attains the level of the higher stream, after which the forward gates are opened and the boat proceeds on its way. The process of lowering a boat is merely the reverse, one of letting water out of the lock.

The most common type of lock gate is the "mitre-gate," which consists of two leaves, suspended on vertical axes from the sidewalls and meeting at an angle in the center of the stream, with the apex toward the upper level of the stream. Wood was formerly used in gate construction, but steel has since supplanted it. The vast improvements in gate design may be realized when we consider the fact that forty-foot lifts are common today, as compared to ten- and twelve-foot maximum lifts of a few years ago.

France indulged in considerable canal construction in the seventeenth century after the introduction of locks. England then followed but did little until the latter half of the eighteenth

Courtesy Illinois Central System

GATUN LOCKS, PANAMA CANAL, AT NIGHT

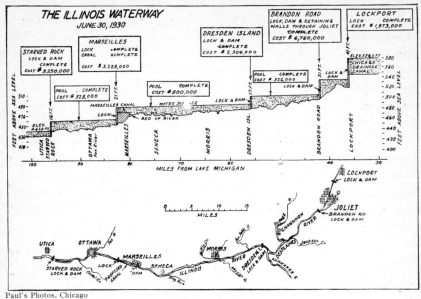

Paul's Photos, Chicago

DIAGRAM OF THE ILLINOIS WATERWAY

century. This country stirred into activity along this line around the early part of the nineteenth century. Of course, the railroads had not yet arrived, and river transportation afforded the only economical means of travel available. In the latter half of the nineteenth century, European countries began to enlarge their canals, but the American awakening to large-scale construction did not occur until the early years of the twentieth century. This revival in canal interest resulted in the Panama Canal and the New York Stage Barge Canal, both federal projects.

The first canal-engineering project in this country was that of circumnavigating the falls of the Connecticut River at South Hadle Falls, Massachusetts, in 1793. This was followed by the construction of the Erie Canal after years of political bickering, which is probably one of the best-known canals in the New York state system. Construction was proposed in 1808, with work finally starting in 1817. After eight years' work it was opened from Albany to Buffalo, three hundred sixty-three miles, with eighty-four locks and a total lift of six hundred eighty-nine feet, at a cost of over seven million dollars. Improvements were added as time went on.

The previously mentioned Illinois-Michigan Canal, which extends from La Salle, Illinois, to the south branch of the Chicago River in Chicago, is ninety-six miles long and has an elevation difference of one hundred forty-five feet. This is provided for by seventeen locks, 110′x18′, each of which will accommodate a boat up to one hundred fifty tons.

The advent of the railroad proved a severe blow to inland water travel and shipping. Here was presented a means of much faster transportation from one place to another. A town did not have to be on a river to prosper. An entirely new industry was being created, which was to become one of the country's foremost, and with it came also a further recession in the frontiers of our nation.

EARLY RAILROADING

The term "railroad" has been applied to many types of construction, but professional engineers limit its use only to such methods of transportation as require rails raised above the ordinary level of the surface, on which are operated vehicles with flanged wheels.

According to this definition, the first railroad was chartered on March 4, 1826, which ran from a granite quarry at Quincy, Massachusetts, to the wharf at the Neponset River. It was con-

Courtesy Baltimore & Ohio R. R.

THE RACE BETWEEN "TOM THUMB" AND A HORSE-DRAWN RAIL COACH

structed for the purpose of transporting the granite that was used in building the Bunker Hill Monument.

The rails were of 6 inch by 12 inch pine timber, topped with a 2 inch by 4 inch oak strip on which there were bar-iron strips 2½ inches wide by ⅝ inch thick for the flanged wheels to run on. The cost was $11,250.00 a mile for a distance of three miles. Two horses pulled the cars uphill; the cars were allowed to run downhill uncontrolled.

The oldest interurban railroad engineering project in the United States, still in service, is the Baltimore and Ohio, which was chartered in 1827 by the State of Maryland. The first section was thirteen miles in length, from Baltimore to Ellicott's Mills, and it was opened in 1830. After experimentation with many types of motive power, including horses and even sails, steam locomotives were put in operation in 1831.

The progress in rails has been from the previously mentioned bar iron fastened to a wood plank to the modern one-hundred-ten-pound per yard rolled steel T-rails. Some rails are of sixty-foot length but those in general use are of thirty-foot length. Much work has been done lately in the welding of rails into one long continuous piece of track without bolt connections.

ROUNDING THE CURVES

The early problems in railroad engineering dealt chiefly with getting rails laid from one town or state to another. There was not so much emphasis placed on roadbed construction, and scientific banking of curves. However, with the introduction of heavier equipment, more attention was required for the proper ballasting of rails, accurate curve construction and banking. This latter is a very important feature when one considers the centrifugal force created by a fast train as it rounds a curve. This may be illustrated by a person swinging a water-filled bucket swiftly in a vertical circle and noting that centrifugal force will keep the water from spilling for the instant the bucket is at the top of its arc. This same theory is applied by engineers in banking curves, so that when a train rounds one at a high speed, the centrifugal force created will merely serve to press the cars tighter to the rails instead of tending to make them go in a straight line rather than take the curve.

The problem of crossing mountains and gorges is perhaps the greatest in the engineering of railroad construction. The odds have, in many cases, seemed unsurmountable but where there is a will there is a way. In some instances, a zig-zag track has been laid up the face of mountains, progressing a certain distance in one direction and then completely reversing the trail at a higher elevation, and continuing the process until the summit is reached, then repeating the wearisome winding to get down on the other side of the mountain. The difficulty of laying a railroad in such rough country may be more fully appreciated when it is realized that a 2-per-cent grade is just about the maximum that a train is capable of negotiating on smooth rails. This means a two-foot rise in elevation for every one hundred feet of horizontal travel. Thus the difficulties that face the construction engineer are indeed trying. When conditions permit, he tunnels through mountains to overcome them. The Moffat Tunnel, situated near the

Courtesy L. & N. R. R.

TUNNEL AT MULLINS, KY., JUST BEFORE COMPLETION

Paul's Photos, Chicago

PHOTO-DIAGRAM OF THE CASCADE TUNNEL

Continental Divide just west of Denver, provided a thrilling engineering achievement. Digging parties started work at both ends of the tunnel, more than six miles apart, and when they met in the center, the center lines of the bores were not more than a fraction of an inch apart. The floor of the tunnel was not level, but varied in grade in different sections, which made the feat all the more amazing.

SAFETY ON THE RAILS

Safety features that engineers have incorporated into our railroad systems merit their share of attention also, and a few shall be mentioned. Perhaps the most important step forward in railroading was the invention and application of the air brake. This was a creation of the engineering genius of George Westinghouse. The air brake made possible higher speeds because of its greater braking power in shorter distances. This also meant that longer trains could be operated with greater safety. The introduction of steel increased the safety factor in collisions; it also increased the weight of the trains, but this was offset by the efficiency of the air brake.

Block signals were another milestone in railroad safety. Steel bridges were erected over right-of-ways, particularly multi-track sections, and signals were installed on these frameworks. The distance between bridges or towers is called a block. If one train is in a block, following trains are either warned of the fact or stopped entirely by means of automatic train controls. These are sometimes called "dead man controls"; they will stop the train if it runs a red signal because of disability of the engineer, or

A RAILWAY
SWITCH TOWER
AND CONTROL
BOARD

negligence, or failure to see the signal. A further safeguard to signals is the installation of a signal board in the locomotive cab that duplicates the signals on the towers. The advantages of this are obvious in the event of fog or other conditions that prevent the signal towers from being seen.

It has been estimated that in traveling between Chicago and Los Angeles, the train will travel over one mile without running on rails, this being the sum of all the distances between rail joints.

Hardly had the railroads been placed on a firm basis, when another method of travel arose to challenge their supremacy, much as they themselves had supplanted river travel. This coincided with the advent of the automobile which gave the United States the finest network of highways in the world.

THE HIGH ROADS AND THE LOW

When the automobile was coming into prominence, the roads that existed were a far cry from the wonderful, easily traveled, ribbons of concrete that we know today. For the most part, they consisted of dirt paths hewn through the fields with little thought given to scientific drainage, grading, or easement over hills.

The engineering of land highways is perhaps one of the oldest of engineering arts. It was not until hills, valleys, cliffs, and bodies of water were overcome that man was able to travel to any great extent. Road building made considerable progress in the heyday of the Roman Empire when practically all the lands conquered by Roman troops were connected by roads whose marvelous and durable construction has enabled many of them to survive to the present day.

The emphasis on the part played by the engineer in road construction was not nearly so marked in early times as it is today. There are very complex problems concerning alignment, curves, width, thickness, and avoidance of obstacles that require expert attention; only the well-trained highway engineer can cope with them. The laxity of using engineering principles is well illustrated in some of the early roads. A king described as the

THE APPIAN WAY LEADING
INTO ROME

Enit photo

"Great King of Egypt" used one hundred thousand men for a period of ten years in the construction of highways across the burning desert sands for the purpose of transporting materials for the pyramids. These roads were massive in construction, being ten feet thick in some places. They were lined on both sides with huge mausoleums, statues, and temples.

The early Romans gave little attention to the matter of economy, because slaves were always available in almost countless numbers. Perhaps the most familiar of old roads was the Appian Way, built by Appius Claudius, a Roman ruler, about 312 B.C.

The principal engineering problem of those times seems to have been the alignment of roads. They were built in straight lines, often surmounting difficult areas that a modern engineer might easily have avoided. The question of economics is much more important, however, now than it was then, and the resourcefulness of contemporary highway engineers may be well illustrated by the reopening and improvement of some of the roads that date back to the Roman conquest of Britain. Most of this activity has been carried on since the year 1920.

England's Parliament passed a road law in 1285 stating that in the construction of a road, trees and shrubs must be cut for a distance of two hundred feet on either side to prevent the concealment of robbers.

Early American roads were called "turnpikes" or toll roads. The first of this type was built in 1785 between Alexandria and Sniggin's Gap. In 1792 the Philadelphia-Lancaster turnpike was the first to be constructed of broken stone. The term "turnpike" is still used, principally in the East, although it does not signify a toll road any more.

ROAD BUILDING MATERIALS

In this country, before 1904, the principal roads were constructed of gravel and dirt, which served their purposes well, since the traffic over them consisted of relatively light, horse-drawn, steel-tired vehicles, and bicycles near a city. Increased motor traffic caused these roads to "ravel," however, and maintenance was almost impossible. The problem then confronting the highway engineer was to produce a road that would stand the abuse of the increased amount and speed of traffic. This was overcome for

Courtesy Swiss Alpine Postal Services.   Photo by Spreng, Basel.

SWISS POSTAL BUSSES ON THE NOTED FURKA ROAD
This road is one of the ancient Alpine passes such as were used by
Hannibal, Caesar and Napoleon.

Courtesy Civic & Commerce Assn., Redwood Falls, Minn.

HIGHWAY BRIDGE INTO REDWOOD FALLS, MINN.

the time by the use of macadam bituminous on rural roads. The macadam road was a type devised in the year 1816 by a Scottish engineer of the same name. He proposed that gravel roads should consist of heavy-stoned base courses and fine stone for surface treatment. To this type of construction was added a bituminous (tar or asphalt) binder and the result was a road commonly known as the "black top" road.

The different types and classes of road building materials an engineer has at his disposal are legion in number and any one of them alone or combinations of them may be used in the construction of a highway. Very often the engineer uses an old gravel or black top road to form the base course for a new concrete surface and excellent results are obtained. Asphalt and other tar surfaces were used to a considerable extent in the building of city streets, but with the tremendous increase the last few years have seen in load-carrying demand, many of the more heavily traveled streets have been re-surfaced with concrete, much after the fashion of highway construction. The asphalt surface is retained in residential sections and even though it presents a more resilient surface than concrete, heavy traffic will soon cause depressions where base weaknesses exist, producing something of a corduroy effect that soon becomes quite an annoyance to the operator of a motor vehicle.

Courtesy Chain Belt Co., Milwaukee

PAVING MACHINE IN OPERATION

Soon after the increase of motor vehicles became apparent, the engineer was faced with the problem of constructing a road of durable surface as well as a substantial base. This led to the use of Portland cement concrete for surfacing, and this type of road is very familiar to all who travel by motor car. The first all-concrete highway ever laid in the United States was at Bellefontaine, Ohio, in 1893. The concrete was poured in block sections, five feet square, which resulted in numerous objectionable joints that experience has proved to be unnecessary. However, the road was well constructed and is still in use. About 1912 the need for this type of highway soon assumed national proportions, and by the year 1923, the work of laying this type of road was progressing at the rate of approximately six thousand miles per year. The majority of the country's concrete roads are to be found in the Middle West, but the work continues in all parts of the nation.

The work of the highway engineer is by no means ended with the selection of proper construction materials. His tasks are vitally connected with numerous phases of road building. The ever increasing amount of motor traffic has made him resort to building pavements of greater width, namely, the three-lane and four-lane highways, the latter in particular. Later on, he decided more safety might be incorporated in highway construction by separating the opposing streams of traffic. This was accomplished by building what is called the divided multi-lane highway, with a parkway running between the two divided sections of the road.

HIGH-SPEED ROADS

Higher speed vehicles brought another challenge to the highway engineer's ingenuity and it was answered with an extensive campaign of grade separations. Now, it is common to see, particularly at the intersection of two heavily-laden roads, a bridge, or highway arch, that permits one road to cross the other at a different elevation. Suitable turning lanes, of course, are installed to allow vehicles of one road to gain access to the other. This grade-separation feature is also receiving much attention in the case of highways crossing railroad tracks, the scenes of countless tragic accidents.

No longer does the modern highway ramble "o'er hill and dale," because the engineer has cut through the crowns of hills and filled in the valleys to provide a road of more uniform elevation. This not only assures more comfortable travel, but decreases the cost of vehicle operation, and most important of all, allows for a greater visibility distance, through the elimination of blind hill crowns.

Curves also have come in for their share of "face lifting" at the hands of the engineer. Roads constructed even as recently as ten or fifteen years ago possess curves that are proving to be too sharp and dangerous for modern high speed travel. As a result many curves have been lengthened and relocated entirely to provide safer travel and greater visibility. Nothing is quite so fraught with danger as blind curves and steep hills, beyond which lies the unknown, too often in more ways than one.

Country of extreme roughness places another demand on the engineer, that of building tunnels as well as roads that will insure

Courtesy General Electric Co.

MODERN STREET LIGHTING IN A WISCONSIN CITY

safe passage. It is very often necessary to bore through a hill or mountain that a road may be carried through rather than around the face of a precipitous cliff.

Another safety feature that has sprung from the fertile brain of the engineer is an improvement in highway lighting. A few test installations have been made of a comparatively new sodium-vapor lamp that provides sufficient illumination without glare that will increase the range of the driver's vision beyond the head-lights. As a matter of fact, powerful headlamps are not necessary when driving over a road equipped with this type of lighting. Details of the highway or obstructions become as visible at night as they are in daytime.

The contrast between ancient and modern transportation reminds one of the query "which was first, the hen or the egg." The building of Roman roads made possible the improvement of vehicles that used them. Now, the situation is reversed, since modern motor cars are far ahead of our roads in design. This probably accounts for the staggering total of automobile casualties. Efforts are being made to make our roads equal to the vehicle, but there is still much to be done, and it is the highway engineer who will play the leading role in this "catching-up" process.

No country has surpassed the United States in the matter of road building, and we have achieved our leadership mainly because of the numbers of automobiles in the country—over 27,000,000 of them.

SHIPS OF THE AIR

About the time the automobile had established itself in the lives of the American people, a new form of travel emerged from the experimental stage and made its bid for national recognition as a quick and efficient means of transportation. This new industry was aviation, and it has provided one of the most romantic and adventurous chapters in the history of man's efforts to move rapidly from one place to another.

The part played by the modern airport is much more than that of just being a landing field for airplanes. It serves as a maintenance and repair station, offers storage facilities, has radio communication with planes aloft, maintains a weather station, has air traffic control, and is connected with other cities, bureaus, and airports by teletypewriter equipment. In addition, restaurants, waiting rooms, and rest rooms are provided for passengers.

These facilities, however, did not always exist for the convenience and safety of air travel. In the early days of aviation, the fields were not as elaborate and completely equipped, and much of the flying, aside from mail transport, was done by "barnstormers" who traveled from town to town selling short rides to the oftentimes bewildered natives of the vicinity. Naturally, these out-of-the-way places possessed no airports, and the wandering airman picked out a nice-looking pasture near town and hoped any unseen ruts would not be too severe as he set his plane down.

AIR NAVIGATION

Early air lanes were not as definitely marked as they are today with radio and lighting equipment. Today, a pilot may fly from one part of the country to another without once seeing the ground, and still reach his destination safely and accurately. This

Photo by H. L. Summerville

ADMINISTRATION BUILDING, RANDOLPH FIELD, SAN ANTONIO

Paul's Photos. Chicago

UP-TO-DATE AIRPORT IN SAN JUAN, PORTO RICO
A mile-long swampy peninsula was filled in and equipped with runways, hangars and shops.

is possible because of the tremendous advances and improvements in radio communication. As long as the aviator remains on his course a steady hum is heard through his radio earphones, but if . he should wander to one side, he would immediately hear a dot-dash signal, or a dash-dot, depending on which way he had strayed. Frequent weather broadcasts also are additional safeguards to flying, these reports being broadcast at frequent intervals throughout the day and night and relaying the most up-to-the-minute weather information from all parts of the country.

THE VEHICLES

Studying the important factors that make it possible to move our modern vehicles of transportation, we must necessarily give much consideration to the vehicles themselves. It is obvious how utterly useless and ridiculous would have been all the improvements in harbors, rails, highways, and airports, if the vehicles that availed themselves of these facilities did not keep step with such advancements and improvements.

THE FIRST BOATS

One of the chief phases of transportation was water travel. At first there were no known methods by which this element could be traversed. Later it was discovered that certain objects could be held up by water, and these objects could be moved through the water and made to carry people and goods. The first attempts were very crude, but as knowledge and skill were gained through the ages, the subject of water transportation afforded many tales of romance, adventure, and discovery of continents. Man's ingenuity in designing vehicles for sea travel has been amazing. Today the marine engineers have provided craft of tremendous size, luxurious appointments and heretofore unequaled factors of safety which have all made water travel more comfortable, convenient, and safe.

The first form of water craft was undoubtedly a log, or a series of logs tied together to form a raft. Man was delighted to find he could move himself and his goods safely across lakes and rivers that had formerly been his barriers, but success breeds discontent, and he wanted to go faster and with less shipping of water. This probably accounted for the hewn-out log that he used as a means of transportation, and which was probably the forerunner of the modern rowboat. Today, the counterpart of the early log still persists in the methods of shipping logs to the sawmills by floating them individually or tied in the form of huge cigar-shaped rafts.

The desire to propel his boat faster gave rise to man's use of a pole to help move his craft through the water. However, the pole outlived its usefulness when the early mariner ventured out over deeper water, and this gave rise to the development of the oar. This is a familiar device, with one end flattened to allow for the application of pressure of the oar against the water.

The use of the oar has survived all the countless years since its inception. One of the earliest uses of it is found in the ancient war galleons which were often of considerable size. These ships were equipped with hundreds of oars which were manned by an equal number of slaves.

MARINE ENGINEERING OF VIKING DAYS

The paddle that is usually associated with American Indian and modern canoes is an adaptation of the oar. Two individuals usually seated at either end of the canoe manipulate one paddle each. This paddle differs from the ordinary oar in that its blade is longer and broader and the handle is somewhat shorter.

Lifeboats on some of our huge ocean liners are equipped with oars for propelling them, as are boats that are used for rescue service by the Coast Guard. These boats are essentially the same in design as the usual type of one-man rowboat with the exception of being considerably larger in size.

Faster means of travel were soon desired and since man had put his own muscular power to the limit of its capabilities he found it necessary to devise mechanical methods of providing more power to move bigger ships at a faster pace.

SAILBOATS

The first of these mechanical means was the use of the sail to make available the power that was in the wind. This method of propulsion also had a humble beginning but rose in efficiency and use to make some of our later ships the prides of nations and objects of breath-taking beauty to behold.

Records of the earliest uses of sails for moving boats and ships through water are found in old paintings and sculptures of Egypt, and even though those boats were equipped with sails, rowers are also visible. The Romans were forced to build and use ships because of the competition from the Carthaginians. The ancient Vikings of the third century built sturdy sailing ships to sail the turbulent, northern seas.

The Genoese, who are generally credited with building and operating the first merchant ships, used sails around the beginning of the fourteenth century, and of course, Christopher Columbus, at the end of the fifteenth century, used sails for motive power on the three ships which carried his expedition that resulted in his discovery of America.

The romantic era of Spanish treasure ships and pirate vessels was ushered in around 1588 when sailing vessels of lengths up to and over 100 feet were making regular trips across the Atlantic, the Spanish ships to get the gold and silver found in the New World, and the pirate ships to take it away from them. One of the largest ships of that day was the "Madre de Dios" captured in 1592 by the English, which had a capacity of 1,600 tons, and was 106 feet long.

Shipbuilding in America started almost as soon as the first colonists arrived, because of the abundance of suitable lumber.

Perhaps the most romantic of sailing vessels were the clipper ships of the past century. Their construction was such that they were as fast as possible with a heavy cargo. Fast freight travel was becoming a necessity along with fast passenger ships, particularly in the transportation of teas, coffees, spices, dried fruits, etc., from oriental ports.

Each year saw larger clipper ships until ten years after the first one was built around 1839, the tonnage had increased from 150 to 2,400. Speeds averaged around six miles per hour and nine miles per hour was considered exceptional, especially with a cargo. The largest clipper ship of all was the "Great Republic," a four-masted ship of 4,555 tons, and built in Boston in 1853. She was 314 feet long.

The peak of sailing ships was reached with the construction of a seven-masted steel schooner, having a displacement of 10,000 tons, and cargo capacity of 7,500 tons. The total sail area was 41,000 square feet.

THE MODERN BOAT

The use of paddle wheels and screws for moving ships was introduced around the beginning of the nineteenth century. The one exception is the record of a paddle wheel on Roman galleys that was operated by hand power through a windlass.

Robert Fulton's "Clermont," built in 1806-7, was the vessel usually classed as the forerunner of modern steam navigation. Huge vertical paddle wheels were fastened to the sides of the boat near the center and their rotation due to steam power propelled the boat through the water.

Courtesy The Alaskan Railroad.   Photo by Rolphe Dauphin.

A PASSENGER STEAMER ON THE YUKON

Courtesy French Steamship Lines

THE "NORMANDIE"

Courtesy Buffalo Museum of Science

ESKIMOS WITH SKIN BOATS (KAYAKS)

Mississippi and Ohio River paddle-wheel boats furnished the river folk with many a hair-raising event because of their memorable races and tragedies. Stern-paddle-wheeled boats are still used on these rivers, preserving some of the most picturesque history that has ever come out of our country's interior.

The next adaptation of steam power was to use a screw or propeller drive at the rear of the hull. This type of power is in use today on our huge liners that regularly ply the waters of the seven seas with clocklike regularity and consistency.

THE DEVELOPMENT OF LAND VEHICLES

Vehicles that travel on land have gone through perhaps one of the most complete and amazing evolutions of any type of transportation. Long before man was able to travel over the water and through the air he was compelled to confine all his traveling activities to the land. He often met unsurmountable obstacles, such as mountains and huge bodies of water, that made his territory rather limited. He had always had a burning desire to conquer these difficulties so he could travel where his fancy dictated, but

Courtesy Buffalo Museum of Science

ESKIMO FOOD CACHE, IGLOO, AND DOG SLED

it was a long, slow process, and often most discouraging. He broadened his scope somewhat when he employed animals as a means of power and transportation, and then as he became more skilled and educated he devised vehicles to carry himself and his possessions over greater distances than he had ever been able to travel before.

Perhaps the vehicle was the brain child of the first "transportation engineers" was the drag, a device that consisted principally of two long tree branches, each tied to an animal's crude harness, with the other ends dragging on the ground behind. Early American Indians availed themselves of this type of travel equipment, and while it undoubtedly possessed more or less bouncing and rough riding qualities, it served its purpose.

Modern sleds and sleighs still adhere to this principle in their runners, and it is not so many years ago that he who owned a fine team of horses and an ornate sleigh was someone who was getting along very nicely in life. Sleighs still are the principal vehicles of transportation in countries that are affected by severe winters, such as far northern countries.

Courtesy Buffalo Museum of Science

MONGOLIAN OX CART AND SEDAN CHAIR

WHEELS

If there is any one reason why transportation has advanced to the point of development that it has today, that one reason may well be the invention, application, and development of the all-important, though too often taken-for-granted, wheel. Without this one piece of rolling equipment, there would not be possible the wonderful transportation mediums we have available today. There would be no automobiles as we have them, or trains, or any other wheeled vehicle, not even the airplane.

Wheels, of course, had to go through the same evolutionary and developing processes that were required of the vehicles which they supported and carried along. The earliest types of wheels were sometimes cut out of solid pieces of wood or were constructed by fastening a number of planks together and cutting out a circular shape. Needless to say, the crude instruments that necessarily must have been used resulted in wheels that did not always possess the smoothest of edges. These wheels were then attached either directly or through an axle to the body of a cart, and there you have the height of transportation facilities among primitive people. All sorts of domesticated animals were pressed into service as motive power, from a dog hauling Dutch milk carts, to huge oxen in India dragging ponderous carts and wagons behind them. The primitive wheel, as described above, is still used in poorer sections of different countries, principally foreign. It was only natural that refinements in the design of wheels should come about as time went on, and it was learned that short rods of wood projecting radially from the hub and encircled by a band resulted in the ordinary spoked wheel that possessed as much strength and durability with less weight.

The next step in the design of carts and wagons was one of providing more comfort, since the roads of a few hundred years ago were merely designed for getting from one place to another and not necessarily for ease of travel. Springs were adopted which isolated the body of the vehicle from direct contact with the axles or wheels; this resulted in a tremendous improvement in riding qualities. Jolts and jars that the wheels suffered were taken up to a considerable extent by the springs, and the majority of the impact force did not reach the body of the vehicle.

Along with the improvement in springs and in material used

"TO MARKET, TO MARKET" IN BELGIAN DOG-CARTS

Courtesy Buffalo Museum of Science

MODELS OF AN EARLY WAGON AND WHEELBARROW

Courtesy Buffalo Museum of Science

MODEL OF A COVERED WAGON OF PIONEER DAYS

Courtesy Buffalo Museum of Science

MODEL OF AN EARLY NEW ENGLAND STAGE COACH

in construction, the size of wagons increased until it became a common sight, before the widespread use of the motor truck, to see huge moving vans rumbling over city streets, often of such size as to require the pulling power of many teams of horses.

THE AUTOMOBILE

The common "one horse-shay" of forty years ago became the foundation of the automobile, many manufacturers merely tacking on a gasoline engine where they could find room for it and connecting it to the wheels through a chain drive. This gave rise to the expression "horseless carriage," and when they encountered trouble, which was very frequent, it also gave rise to the expression, "Get a horse." However, the early automotive pioneers refused to be daunted, and their courage and spirit have given us the modern automobile that possesses such amazing capabilities.

Automotive engineers then transformed the automobile into an all-weather vehicle with the introduction of closed bodies. All the while, mechanical reliability was attaining greater perfection.

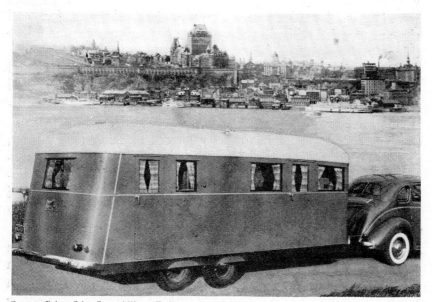

Courtesy Robert Crist, Covered Wagon Trailers

"HOTEL ON WHEELS"—THE AUTO TRAILER

XIV—10

INTERIOR OF A
MODERN AUTO
TRAILER

Courtesy Robert Crist,
Covered Wagon Trailers.

The self-starter, invented by Kettering, increased the range of
users, making it controllable by women, and with its ever increasing popularity, roads were being built and improved; so it was not
very long before all America was spinning on wheels. Engines
were improved, made more powerful, quiet, and economical, and
the construction of bodies of steel was becoming a commonplace
thing.

Every device for the improvement, increased comfort, and
ease of operation known to automotive engineers was incorporated
in succeeding models, until now we have as a climax an automobile that is air-conditioned.

More and more people every year are hitching their homes,
in the form of trailers, to the back bumpers of their cars and driving them across the highways of the nation. Today, the "horseless carriage" has grown to be one of the leading industries of
the nation and is assuming the role of a barometer of prosperity
and depression.

The improvement and progress of automotive engineering
have provided the American family with an economical medium
for traveling. People are finding it infinitely cheaper to jump in
the family car and take a trip over smooth highways, even across
the entire nation.

THE STREETCAR

In the days before the advent of the automobile, railroads, interurban and urban, had things fairly much their own way. They did not, however, allow this to stop them from improving equipment and service. Horse-drawn streetcars and railways gave way to electricity and steam power.

Before the application of electric motors to streetcars, however, a system of cables was employed. Endless ropes traveled in slots beneath the street surface and between the two rails that the car ran over. A gripping bar extended down from the car and through the slot in the street where it could grip or release the moving cable through mechanism operated by the motorman of the car. These cables traveled at definite speeds; through congested areas at a moderate pace; in outlying districts faster cables were used. The motorman could operate his car at a speed slower than the cable by merely applying the gripping in-

Ewing Galloway photo

A TROLLEY CAR IN SANTIAGO, CHILI

Courtesy San Francisco Chamber of Commerce

CABLE CARS IN SAN FRANCISCO
In several hilly cities of the United States these cable cars are used on grades
too steep for ordinary trolleys.

struments lightly, allowing the cable partially to slip through and
partially pull the grip.

Electric motors were finally adapted to street railway vehicles,
and that is the power generally in use today. Improvement in

equipment has resulted in lighter weight cars of streamline design and superior braking characteristics. These advancements have been made in an effort to modernize and speed up service to compete with automobile transportation in cities.

Street railways have not always indulged in the sole occupation of transporting passengers from one part of a city to another. There was a time in the city of Chicago when the street car companies owned and operated cars for the delivery of United States Mail about the city.

ELEVATEDS AND SUBWAYS

There are two other types of urban railroad transportation and they are elevated and subway trains. These trains are usually of many cars and operate on overhead structures or through tunnels beneath the surface of the ground. The first type of motive power that was used to pull elevated trains was the ordinary steam locomotive. Acceleration, deceleration, and service in general were comparatively slow with this type of power, and electric motors were substituted on the cars themselves. The advantages of this type of transportation are obvious, there being no traffic to contend with, higher speeds, and a more resilient foundation for the tracks, whereas streetcar rails are usually laid in concrete, which will provide very little springing effect.

Attempts have been made to run streetcars in multi-car units, and the system was fairly successful years ago when the cars were smaller than the present models and traffic congestion was unknown. Efforts to run this type of equipment under present-day conditions have resulted in slower service and street blocking. Single-car units for street operation are more flexible and their size conforms better to the room available.

SPEED ON THE RAILROADS

In the field of long-distance transportation, there has been almost every means used from the old "prairie schooner" to the latest 5,400 horse-power, streamlined, Diesel-electric train. The adventures of early pioneers provided us with many a hair-raising tale as we followed them across hills and plains, through all kinds

Courtesy Union Pacific Railroad

EVOLUTION IN RAILWAY TRANSPORTATION
A Union Pacific Streamliner alongside old "Number Nine."

of weather, and even, in our imagination, helped get the wagon train into a circle to pick off the attacking hordes of Indians. After these pioneers had blazed their trails, the railroads pushed farther and farther into the West, and they also had Indian trouble. During the construction work there were probably as many Indians fired at as there were rail spikes driven into ties.

Courtesy Greyhound Lines

STREAMLINED BUS FOR HIGHWAY TRAVEL

The railroads had long-distance transportation all to themselves for many years. However, the increased use of the automobile, motor truck, and airplane, began to eat into their business and it took them about ten years to do something about it.

The railroads' answer to the challenge of faster and cheaper means of travel was the introduction of high-speed freight service and the development of modern streamliners, the latter of which has gone ahead by leaps and bounds. The Union Pacific furnishes a striking illustration of this progress. In 1933, their first effort in this new field was a 900 H. P. three-car Diesel-electric train, the whole of which weighed about as much as a standard Pullman coach. In 1937, four years later, they had twin trains for Chicago to California service, of 5,400 horse-power and comprising seventeen cars each, three of which are needed to house the motive equipment. The trains are each about $\frac{1}{4}$ mile long and can maintain speeds of 110 miles per hour. Other railroads, of course, are making similar steps to recapture the traveling public's fancy that they once held.

The engineering behind modern streamlined trains represents some of the most brilliant thought ever applied to transportation. It was known that a high-speed train was needed and many ways were possible to attain this end. The first was to build a train of as little wind resistance as possible. This was accomplished by wind-tunnel tests, an idea borrowed from the aviation industry, in which models could be observed for their behavior and characteristics in regard to wind resistance. After the shape was decided on, the question turned to one of light materials for its construction. This was the first step toward higher speed, the eliminating of useless weight. Then it was found that the Diesel-driven electric generators could provide the necessary power for the motors to attain the desired speeds.

The successive improvements in streamlined trains have not been in regard to a greater degree of streamlining, but mostly in connection with longer trains, or more power and more luxurious appointments. The same inherent aerodynamic principles of the early trains were so well engineered that improvements along this line have not been necessary.

One revolutionary aspect of construction in streamlined trains is that found on the cars, namely the articulated coach. This articulation of cars deviates from the common practice of each railroad car having its own two sets of trucks. The articulated coach is so built that the connecting ends of two cars rest on the same set of trucks, which is placed directly beneath where the couplings of ordinary coaches would be located.

As stated before, one of the main reasons for such feverish activity on the part of the railroads to furnish high-speed service has been the amazing success and efficiency of modern air travel.

SHIPS OF THE AIR

Aviation, as we have it today, represents one of the most rapidly developed industries that has assumed major proportions. It is the work of pioneering, far-seeing men who had the courage to back up their convictions and stand by their work while the general public hesitated to accept this new form of transportation.

The birds of the air in their free and easy flight through space have been the envy of man for ages, and one of his most burning desires was to emulate them, but when the opportunity arrived, very few took advantage of it. The World War was perhaps the greatest impetus aeronautical science received. In the first days of the conflict, ancient-looking planes were used very little, small emphasis being placed on their value as fighting weapons, but four years later found the airplane one of the most formidable fighting machines the opposing forces had at their command.

The radical changes in design and performance of war planes were such that, if compared, post-war and pre-war planes might appear to belong to different ages.

BALLOONS AND ZEPPELINS

One type of lighter-than-air craft that was actually rowed through the air was built in 1784 by the Robert brothers. The balloon was melon-shaped and inflated with pure hydrogen. A car was suspended beneath the bag, and a crew of six used silken oars which they manipulated as if they were rowing a boat. It

APPLYING OUTER COVER TO A ZEP-PELIN TYPE AIR-CRAFT

Courtesy Goodyear Tire & Rubber Co.

took seven hours to travel over a circle about one kilometer in radius.

The art of building lighter-than-air craft was put on a substantial basis around the turn of the present century by Santos-Dumont, a Brazilian living in Paris, and Ferdinand von Zeppelin, a German enthusiast. Airships and balloons were used extensively during the Great War for scouting, observation, and raiding, the famous London air raids by Zeppelins proving them to be an efficient long-range weapon of aerial fighting.

American authorities did not engage in airship building immediately but sat back and watched developments abroad. They preferred to profit by the others' mistakes before venturing into the manufacture of aircraft to any great extent.

The unfortunate note in lighter-than-air craft history is the series of disasters which have followed in the wake of building apparently fool-proof machines. American-built dirigibles and balloons have fallen victim to most unfortunate accidents. Foreign dirigibles, principally German, have in recent years made amazing records for trans-oceanic travel. The *Los Angeles*, built by Germany and commissioned to the United States in 1924, gave eight years of uninterrupted service to the U. S. Navy, finally being retired in 1932.

On the other hand, we have had three American attempts at dirigible construction, and all have ended in disaster; they were the *Shenandoah*, *Akron*, and *Macon*. The fate of these ships caused the United States to abandon any further activities, at least for the time being, in lighter-than-air craft construction.

The latest German airship, the *Hindenburg*, achieved an admirable record of transatlantic service before its explosion at Lakehurst, N. J., in 1937. Its ocean crossings were becoming so commonplace that newspaper recognition of the feats dwindled to almost nothing. However, it once again crashed the headlines with sickening force when the craft went up in flames without warning at 6 p.m. one afternoon as it was nosing in to the mooring-mast of the Lakehurst airdrome. The *Hindenburg* was the largest airship afloat, its capacity being 7,070,000 cubic feet. It was filled with inflammable hydrogen, the only lifting medium then available to countries other than the United States. We have a process by which non-inflammable helium may be extracted for use in airships.

American airship disasters, however, did not result from fires, but from structural weaknesses in design. Our helium extraction process is naturally one we should hesitate to share with other countries, lest it prove a boomerang in case of future wars. England, however, has discovered a process for the production of this gas and activity in airship building may commence again. Germany has in the process of construction the LZ-130 and LZ-131, successors to the *Hindenburg* (LZ-129). Their construction is of much lighter weight which is a necessity because of the lower lifting power of helium as compared to hydrogen. The *Graf Zeppelin* (LZ-128), since its construction is not suited to the use of helium, has been retired, as has the *Los Angeles* in America. The "Graf" will be on exhibition for a short while, and then be junked. Its record is very imposing, 590 flights since being placed in operation in 1928, 143 of which were trans-oceanic, mostly over the south Atlantic.

HEAVIER-THAN-AIR SHIPS

Along with this type of aviation, we have another class of flying which is by no means less important, since it forms practically the entire scope of aeronautical activity at present. That branch of flying is known as the heavier-than-air class, or the modern airplane.

There are strictly two divisions in the heavier-than-air classification of airplanes, namely the type requiring power to pull and sustain a craft in flight, and the type known as glider. The latter requires an initial impetus of some sort to take off, and then through skilful operation is made to remain aloft by means of using up-current of air. There were adherents to both theories long before the Wright brothers' first powered flight was accomplished in 1903.

Early experimenters, though they did not accomplish actual flight, did evolve more or less of a foundation on which modern aeronautical science is based. They were also divided into two

LAUNCHING A MOTORLESS GLIDER

Science and engineering skill combine with daring to make this sport contribute to aeronautical knowledge.

Paul's Photos. Chicago

groups, exponents of the gliding flight and exponents of powered flight. Otto Lilienthal and two followers, Pilcher of England, and Octave Chanute of the United States adhered to the gliding type of flight. Lilienthal actually made gliding flight a science and defined the value of arched wings.

The second group, or adherents of powered flight, included Clement Ader of France, Sir Hiram Maxim of England, and Samuel P. Langley of the United States. All built powered models with financial assistance from their governments, but this was withdrawn when the efforts of the three proved failures.

The development of the airplane was breath-taking and, as previously mentioned, the World War produced a plane of remarkable efficiency and performance.

DEVELOPMENT OF THE AIRPLANE

Up to and including the period of the war, wood was the chief material used in the construction of airplanes, principally because of its high strength-weight ratio. The one drawback was

Paul's Photos, Chicago

A. E. F. MECHANICS OPERATE ON CRIPPLES

World War emergencies contributed a great deal to the advancement of aviation. Here army workmen are salvaging parts for use in other planes.

PILOTS' COCKPIT
AND INSTRUMENT
PANEL IN MOD-
ERN DUAL CON-
TROL AIR LINER

Courtesy United Air Lines

that straight-grained wood was essential for best results in airplane construction. The vast demands made by the war soon
depleted the supply of this grade of wood, and it was then that
metal was introduced as a construction material.

Aluminum alloys were experimented with at first because of
strength and lightness. The American plane manufacturers were
rather slow to adopt the use of metal, and it was 1922 before
much consideration was given this method of building planes.

Metal construction paved the way for the wholesale streamlining that soon became common. Wires and struts that formerly
were used for bracing wings and under-carriages became unnecessary with the introduction of cantilever wing construction.
This is a method by which the internal wing members are so
built as to make the wing a self-supporting member. The metal
of the fuselage skin covering also carries many of the stresses

of the framework doing away with more "stick and wire" construction.

Retractable landing gears have also come into use to further the streamline principle. After a ship has taken off, the pilot may, upon reaching a certain minimum altitude, operate the mechanism which will pull the landing gear up into recesses in the under side of the wings. When descending, a warning noise tells the pilot that his wheels are still up, should he go below the minimum altitude without lowering the undercarriage.

Modern aviation has become what it is today through the endorsement of the public and the ceaseless efforts of aeronautical engineers who are constantly pitting the maximum of their ingenuity against the mysteries of the science of flying.

Numerous inventions have served to enable aviation to forge ahead and hand in hand do some of the wonderful feats that have been performed with planes that aroused the adulation, curiosity, and interest of the public at large.

The world almost went crazy, America in particular, on May 21, 1927 when a lanky, unknown, mail pilot named "Slim" Lindbergh landed his trim, little monoplane *Spirit of St. Louis* on Le Bourget Field near Paris, after 33 hours of flying over the Atlantic Ocean from New York.

The second great impetus was thus given the art and science of flying. Trans-oceanic flying became the fad and many flights were attempted, some successful, and some ill-fated. Barnstorming aviators, the lone wolves of flying, traveled the length and breadth of the nation selling joy-rides to many who had never seen a plane before.

Accidents occurred, many of them, and the ones that earned newspaper space, and those that still do, are somewhat dampening to the flying enthusiasm of the public in general.

Contrary to common belief, the transatlantic and polar flights that followed Lindbergh's epochal hop to Paris, were not merely stunts, nor done for publicity's sake alone. Even those ships, if placed alongside modern transport planes would appear antiquated. The reason is that aeronautical engineers learned much from those spectacular flights to enable them to return to

FUSELAGE INTERI-
OR OF 21-PASSEN-
GER DOUGLAS
PLANE

View shows mechan-
ics putting the finish-
ing touches on the
skeleton of the big
ship.

Courtesy
American Airlines, Inc.

their drawing boards and design ships of even greater possibilities. Weaknesses in design were revealed and research was begun in an effort to secure even more durable construction materials. Greater safety measures were devised and planes were increased in size. Even in those days when transatlantic flights made page one of every newspaper, we still thought commercial ocean flying was far removed, but today we have the Clippers of Pan-American Airways crossing the Pacific on regular schedules. Non-stop, four-hour service is now available between Chicago and New York in planes that provide the latest in safety, luxury, and efficiency.

Aviation is a young industry, not yet forty years old, and has just about reached its "growing pains" stage. Planes are being built with a greater margin of safety, and radio has proved an invaluable aid, along with the development and progress of modern flying instruments.

There are a number of airlines in existence today that are establishing and maintaining remarkable records of efficiency, performance, and most important of all, safety. But, wonderful as modern aviation is, there is still a long road to travel before the art of flying will reach its millennium.

VEHICLES AND THE HIGHWAY

The work of the highway engineer continues ceaselessly even after he has built the railroad or highway over which train or motor vehicles are to run. However, it is a different class of engineer who comes upon the scene at such a time; he is the maintenance engineer. His job is to keep the highway in good repair to insure the safe passage of its users. He must do all in his power to keep the right-of-way from deteriorating and thus avoid accidents due to damaged rails or pavements.

The maintenance engineer decides whether a road has served its purpose and made a fair return on the investment in its construction and upkeep. Roads, like everything else, will wear out with use; they must be replaced or at least rehabilitated. There are two methods of returning a road to a condition where it can again render useful service, and these are resurfacing the old road, or constructing an entirely new one.

If the original road has an unusually well constructed and well preserved base, it may be more economical to use this old pavement as a base course for a new surface. This has been done in many instances and has been highly successful. The engineer's job is, after all, one of constructing an economically sound project as well as a scientifically sound one. Hence, he is always on the alert to do the best job at the lowest cost. In public works projects, such as highways, the economies or extravagance of the engineer are reflected in the taxes of the community.

The subject of highway loading is a very important one, especially when a new road is to be built. The first procedure of the engineer is to survey the traffic situation over the proposed route. He must know the approximate number of vehicles which will use the road, and also the weight of these vehicles. Some roads are heavily traveled by large trucks and others carry little trucking. He must also determine the time of day when travel is the heaviest, so that proper safety measures may be incorporated in the construction. It is obvious that if the engineer did not take heed of the foregoing features and merely designed a road strong enough to carry passenger automobiles, he and his work would

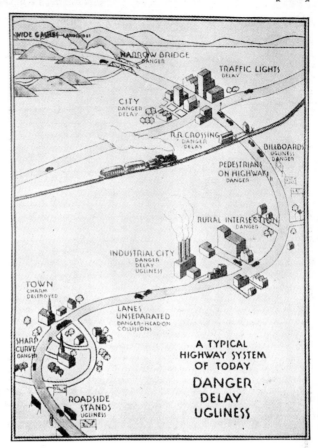

WIDE GATES LANDSCAPES
NARROW BRIDGE DANGER
TRAFFIC LIGHTS DELAY
CITY DANGER DELAY
R.R. CROSSING DANGER DELAY
BILLBOARDS UGLINESS DANGER
PEDESTRIANS ON HIGHWAY DANGER
RURAL INTERSECTION DANGER
INDUSTRIAL CITY DANGER DELAY UGLINESS
TOWN CHARM DESTROYED
LANES UNSEPARATED DANGER-HEAD-ON COLLISIONS
SHARP CURVE DANGER
ROADSIDE STANDS UGLINESS

A TYPICAL
HIGHWAY SYSTEM
OF TODAY
DANGER
DELAY
UGLINESS

DIAGRAM SHOW-
ING HIGHWAY
DANGER SPOTS

Courtesy National
Resources Committee

shortly come to grief when heavy trucks and busses started tearing
it to pieces.

HIGHWAYS AND THE WEATHER

The question of highway drainage is also one of the foremost
in road building. Water on the surface of an earth road will soften
it and cause formation of ruts which can be unpleasant and even
dangerous. Water on a paved surface is equally objectionable,
though for different reasons. Here it can cause the erosion of the
surface due to the action of traffic and will soon lead to a condi-

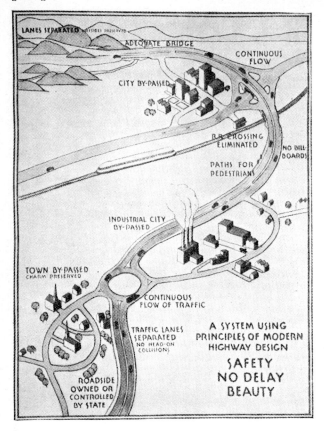

GRAPHIC PRESEN-
TATION OF MOD-
ERN HIGHWAY
DESIGN

Courtesy National
Resources Committee

tion which will require expensive resurfacing. Water is especially harmful when it collects beneath the roadway where it can soften the bed and result in serious depressions and breaking up of the pavement. In cold weather this water will freeze, causing an up-heaval of the roadbed.

In order to forestall these possibilities the engineer resorts to methods of drainage, of which there are three kinds: first, longi-tudinal ditches and gutters for removing water from the road surface; second, culverts and bridges for carrying water through an embankment; and third, various kinds of pipe and stone-filled trenches that will carry away water from the roadbed.

Washouts present another source of worry to the highway

maintenance engineer when surging waters or a torrential rainstorm may carry an entire section of highway before it. The necessary repairs result in the construction of practically a new road for the section that has been washed out, because in the event of extensive damage, the entire surface, roadbed and all might be carried away. Swollen rivers sometimes exact a heavy toll when they batter down a highway bridge, oftentimes destroying the abutments and bridge piers also.

Extreme snow storms in winter may prevent the use of a highway until the snow has been removed. Snow plows and crews must at once go out when a storm assumes such proportions that it threatens to choke up the road. The damage of drifting snow has been somewhat alleviated by the engineer through snow fences placed some distance back off the road to prevent the drifts from spreading to the roadways. These fences vary somewhat, often resembling an ordinary picket fence, with the pickets being fairly thin and set close together. Then when the drift comes sweeping across an open field, it is checked by this fence and prevented from reaching the highway. This has proved to be quite an economy in road maintenance, since it is not necessary to call out the snow plows after every storm.

It can thus be realized that the maintenance engineers fill a role equally as important and vital as that of the construction

Union Pacific Railroad photo

CROWN POINT, ON THE COLUMBIA RIVER HIGHWAY

engineers who undertook to build the road in the first place. With very little stretching of the imagination, one can understand what a severe blow would be dealt the transportation of the country if its highways, which are literally bood streams of the nation, were allowed to deteriorate until they became unfit for travel. Cities which they serve would soon find themselves more or less isolated if travelers could not make their way over the roads with comparative ease and a reasonable degree of safety.

It is also the duty of the maintenance engineers to attempt to bring the highways up to the standard of modern automobiles, so that our high speed cars can operate safely over the roads of the country.

THE MAINTENANCE OF RAILROADS

The railroads, as well as the highway departments, also find it necessary to retain a maintenance department to insure the highest degree of working perfection of their equipment and of the highways over which they travel. Here the principal attention is not given to a surfacing material as in a road, but to steel rails which support the locomotives and cars.

Entire coaches that are elaborately equipped with every possible testing instrument are used by railroads for a number of purposes. It is possible to hook this car to an ordinary train and obtain tests of the rails during actual train operation. This kind of test proves of much more value than laboratory testing work since the behavior of rails can be observed under actual working conditions. The performance of the train itself, locomotive and cars, can also be watched, from which conclusions may be drawn that will further increase the efficiency of train operation. The roadbed and ballast supporting the rails and ties can also be minutely inspected in order that any irregularity may be caught before serious consequences result.

Railroad accidents of course must be followed up, in so far as roadbed condition is concerned, with a most minute inspection. Even if the rails have not been torn up, it is necessary for the engineer to make a very close examination of the roadbed, ties, rails, and rail connections. Perhaps a rail might have developed an internal crack that would cause a break when a future train passed over it. The rail connections must be examined to see that they are still secure to prevent a possible rail spreading under the tremendous pressure exerted by a train. When an accident has occurred, the roadbed is almost always torn up to some extent and this will require repair work in at least part, or perhaps the entire rebuilding of a roadbed section.

The reinforcement of roadbeds becomes necessary with the introduction of streamlined trains. The tremendous speeds of these new trains require that alignment be more perfect than ever both horizontally and vertically. Soft spots in the roadbed would result in an up and down vibration of the train which would not only be uncomfortable, but above all, unsafe. Rails laid in a zig-zag manner, even though the degree of wave be ever so slight, would cause serious sidesway that might increase to such an extent as to throw the train off the rails. It is also necessary to bank the curves more steeply and provide for a greater degree of rail anchorage to prevent spreading when a streamliner enters a curve at high speed.

OLD AND NEW RAILROAD BRIDGES OVER THE OHIO RIVER AT HENDERSON, KY.

Courtesy Louisville and Nashville R. R.

The advent of heavier and faster trains resulted in the reinforcement or new construction of practically all the railroad bridges. In some instances, bridges were built of such size in the first place that they were able successfully to handle the new conditions of greater weight and higher speed. The engineer in designing his bridge must take into account the speed as well as the weight of the vehicle it is intended for. The high speed train upon entering a bridge exerts a terrific impact force upon the structure in addition to the force of its weight.

A good bridge designer is capable of making provisions in his plans that will allow for future improvements and reinforcements as the demands increase. On the other hand there are also situations which would not justify such a procedure, such as a small bridge across a creek. Here it would be cheaper to replace the bridge with a stronger structure than attempt an elaborate one which may be improved upon at a later date. The maintenance engineer is responsible for the upkeep of bridges to see that rust does not eat away a vital joint or that some other unsafe condition does not develop or exist. Many tragic accidents have happened as the result of bridge collapses, and naturally they are a reflection on somebody. The conscientious engineer does not want an accusing finger pointed at him, so he will take all the steps he can think of to prevent such an occurrence.

Frozen switches in the winter time can cause the pile-up of an entire train with very serious consequences. The chief of maintenance must see that his men keep all switches open and in operating order to prevent just such a thing from happening. Torches are sometimes resorted to in an effort to keep the switches warm enough to prevent any snow or moisture from freezing. The all-important thing that is uppermost in the mind of the maintenance men is that the trains must get through, and they must get through safely and on time if possible.

Washouts may result from the same sources and have the same consequences with respect to railroads as to vehicle highways. Entire roadbeds have been washed away, leaving the rails hanging in the air. There have been instances also of so much water seeping into the roadbed that it gave way when a train passed over it. Perhaps one of the rarest incidents in the world today is to

International News photo

OPENING OF THE SAN FRANCISCO-OAKLAND BAY BRIDGE
This span of steel and concrete, over four miles long, represents another
triumph for modern engineering.

take a train trip of any length and not see a track crew at work along some stretch of the road. Their presence does not necessarily mean that trouble has developed, but it means they are looking for trouble and for places where an irregularity might occur. These men are assigned to sections and do nothing but travel up and down their section constantly looking for things that might be fixed. Thus it is possible to nip any trouble before it has a chance to assume serious proportions.

The continual re-ballasting of roadbeds is perhaps the chief routine function of a railroad's maintenance force. As previously mentioned, streamliners have required that much re-ballasting be done, but just as a routine procedure, these crews are constantly fixing up the roadbeds, making them just a little better, tightening up rail joints, and seeing that switches are always in proper working order.

Courtesy Spokane Chamber of Commerce

ARCH OF MONROE STREET BRIDGE ACROSS SPOKANE FALLS

THE ENGINEERING OF BUILDINGS

THE PROTECTION OF A HOME

MAN'S FIRST STRUCTURES served to protect him from the ravages of the weather, from the attacks of wild beasts and sometimes his fellow men. Originally caves, dugouts, and even trees served as his shelter; at times whole colonies of men dwelt in the cliffs. But these natural habitations were not always available, nor was the protection they afforded always adequate. At an early period man began to fashion for himself crude dwelling places. A roof of a sort, walls, and an opening through which to crawl in and out—such was his home. He was not concerned with its appearance. Survival was the important thing to him, and buildings were primarily an expression of the will to live.

Sometimes, for further protection, he fashioned huts raised above the ground on poles; or, as in the Swiss and Italian lakes, he set pile dwellings above water. The remains of whole villages of such structures still exist.

Even the tombs and the religious monuments, erected long before the beginning of history, reflected primitive man's desire for protection, his wish to survive. Sepulchers were often considered a defense against hostile spirits, even against death itself; and places of worship were built to placate the gods, who were not above bribery and might send good weather or successful hunting in exchange.

Through the centuries, the fundamental purpose of buildings has not really changed; their main function remains, in one form or another, a protective one. But naturally, as man's existence has grown more complex, so have his buildings and the uses to which they have been put.

Courtesy Buffalo Museum of Science
MODEL OF ADOBE HOUSE, SOUTHWESTERN UNITED STATES

BUILDINGS AND ENVIRONMENT

The development of buildings parallels the cultural development of man. In the ages of bronze and iron, the discovery of the art of working metals made possible improvements in carpentry and masonry. Superior villages with walls and moats sprang up in the Po Valley. Huts assumed a rectangular shape. Invariably buildings were designed to cope with the climates in which they were erected. In the northern regions, steep roofs disposed of the rain and snow; deep foundations and solid materials combated frost. In the warm and rainless south, flat roofs sloping gently, were built. Thick walls and small windows to keep out heat were used in the hot and sunny regions.

Building design was, of course, influenced by other factors than the weather. Availability of building materials, structural conveniences, communal urges, the desire for artistic expression—all have had a direct and significant influence upon the science and art of building.

Whatever wonder we feel regarding ancient structures, is ordinarily occasioned by the *method* of construction and not by the

materials used. The way in which early man handled his building materials is often difficult to understand, but not the way in
which he obtained them. He took what materials were offered
by the region in which he dwelt and he adapted his buildings to
the demands of these materials. Thus, in some sections of northern Europe the earliest buildings made considerable use of wood,
a material easily available in the great forest regions; whereas in
the Nile Valley homes were first built of clay, and later, on a
larger scale with the excellent stone furnished by the cliffs in that
region.

In Babylonia and Assyria, where stone and wood were scarce
and difficult to find, buildings were commonly constructed with
sun-dried mud brick. Naturally, the materials used influenced the
building designs to a considerable extent. In the case of sun-dried
mud brick, for example, the arch was the only device which
could sustain a great weight while covering a void; hence the
arch's common usage in Mesopotamian buildings. Not until late
in the history of building were structures relatively free from the
influence of local materials.

TEPEE OF SKINS

Courtesy The Art Institute of Chicago
THE TEMPLE, HALL AND COLONNADE OF AMENHOTEP III
AS SEEN FROM ACROSS THE NILE

PURPOSE, DESIGN, AND ART

Structural conveniences played an important part. A building consisting of a roof, walls, and a door, did not meet man's wants for long. He added windows and chimneys for comfort, interior partitions for privacy. As rooms in the buildings became numerous, there arose the problem of providing adequate light

Courtesy Las Vegas Chamber of Commerce
THE "LOST CITY" OF NEVADA

and convenient intercommunication. Sometimes to meet the lighting problem, rooms were grouped about interior courts, and from this practice a particular style of architecture developed. Stairhalls and corridors made possible a means of communication which avoided the disturbing of individual apartments. To meet further requirements buildings were divided into different portions. New needs fathered new designs.

Similarly, community life necessitated new structures. Provision for living quarters and food storage space ceased to be the only concern. Shops, theaters, temples, military structures, and schools came into being; and each type of building led to a particular design. Primitive functionalism existed.

Also, in buildings man found the opportunity for artistic expression. The impulse which had once inspired him to draw crude animals on the walls of caves, directed him to the decoration of the buildings he created. He sought to distinguish his structures, to brighten them; he experimented with new designs. And with the desire to beautify the barren forms came the development of architecture, the art of combining beauty and utility in buildings.

ANCIENT ARCHITECTURE

A major portion of our knowledge of early civilizations is derived from a study of their buildings. In Egypt, the chief buildings of any permanence were temples and tombs. Beginning as mere chambers in the sand, the tombs developed into great pyramids housing the royal dead. The peristyle court, a feature later adopted in Greece and Rome, was a characteristic of the temples. These great courts were surrounded by finely proportioned, fluted and reeded columns, set upon platforms and terraces; columns, stemming from primitive post and lintel construction, were a direct solution to the problem of supporting great weights. The buildings were sumptuous, well planned, and of a majestic scale. They were the products of a civilization vain, imaginative, and despotic.

In the Tigris-Euphrates Valley, the chief buildings of the Babylonian, Assyrian, and Persian cultures were palaces, temples, and tombs. The Babylonian structures were massive but lacking

RESTORATION OF THE ZIGGURRAT AT UR

MODEL OF DELPHI, ABOUT 160 A. D., SHOWING DETAIL
OF THE TEMPLE OF APOLLO

[174]

Courtesy Metropolitan Museum of Art, New York City

THE ROMAN GARDEN—MODEL IN METROPOLITAN MUSEUM
OF ART, NEW YORK

in form. The great Assyrian palaces showed Egyptian influences, significant of the commerce developing in the East. The Persian architecture also showed the increasing effects of commercial contacts.

In Greece, building achieved its purest classical form. To this day use is still made of the Doric, Ionic, and Corinthian orders. The Greek temples are, from an architectural point of view, among the finest structures the world has known, if not the finest. Their graceful simplicity and sense of proportion, the careful, almost mathematical consideration of every detail, their delicate and exquisite ornamentation, bear witness to the infinite care and the art-loving qualities of the builders. A famous modern architect has said, "The Greek Temple means to architecture what Bach means to music."

The buildings of Rome were the product of a people essentially practical, military, and motivated by a sense of their own importance. Structures of mammoth size and great engineering skill abounded. The luxury of the period is reflected in the lavishness

Courtesy J. Bradford Pengelly
INTERIOR OF SANTA SOPHIA, ISTANBUL, TURKEY

of the buildings. The Baths of Caracalla, for example, were fifteen hundred feet long and twelve hundred feet wide, and were decorated with gilded bronze, marble and mosaics. At the same time the Romans were responsible for the developing of many architectural forms, among them the arch, the vault, and the dome.

FROM ROMANESQUE TO RENAISSANCE

The best early Christian architecture is to be found in the East, where a new style was created in which the dome, in unison with the Roman arch, and vault, produced buildings of remarkable beauty. The finest examples of this period are Santa Sophia or Hagia Sophia in Constantinople. The style is called Byzantine; it was later to have considerable influence upon the Romanesque work of France, England, Spain, and Germany.

In Europe, during the tenth and eleventh centuries, Romanesque architecture was much affected by the desire to make basilican churches as nearly fireproof as possible. Losses had been sustained from the burning of early crude basilicas, and the builders now hit upon the idea of applying the Roman type of masonry vault to the basilica. Romanesque architecture developed simul-

WILLIAM'S GATE, CHARTRES, FRANCE

Courtesy The Art Institute of Chicago

THE CATHEDRAL OF NOTRE DAME, CHARTRES, FRANCE

taneously with the solving of this problem and with the need of producing a church with adequate area for window lighting.

The seeds of Gothic architecture were incorporated in the Romanesque style. The controlling feature of the Gothic was the development of the vault for the purpose of spanning new heights. The essential problem was the supporting and buttressing of the higher vaults, and the permitting of clerestory windows at the same time. The solution of this problem came with the use of isolated piers, the perfection of ribbed vaulting, the construction of larger windows, and the application of the pointed arch supported by flying buttresses. The style reached its heights in such structures as Chartres Cathedral and the Cathedral of Notre Dame at Amiens.

The new emphasis upon the importance of man as an individual, the discovery of the old world as well as of the new, and the revival of classical forms, are reflected in Renaissance buildings. Architects, unlike those of the Middle Ages, became known

Courtesy J. Bradford Pengelly

THE DUOMO, FLORENCE, ITALY

Courtesy The Art Institute of Chicago

ST. PAUL'S CATHEDRAL IN LONDON

COLONIAL HOMES OF THE OLD SOUTH
ARLINGTON, VIRGINIA

COLONIAL HOMES OF THE OLD SOUTH
PRINGLE HOUSE, CHARLESTON, S. C.

MOUNT VERNON, FAIRFAX COUNTY, VIRGINIA

MOUNT AIRY, VIRGINIA

by name and their work reflects their individuality. Brunelleschi, Alberti, Bramante, and Michelangelo are among the best known exponents of Renaissance building. An architecture of great beauty, richness, and versatility was developed. Many materials were used lavishly: brick, volcanic stone, common stone, marble, bronze, silver, and even gold. Great advances were made in interior decorations; murals and ceiling designs achieved an artistic excellence never since equaled. New life came to building.

The Renaissance, starting in Italy, found its way into Spain, England, Germany, and France. The European countries developed Renaissance architecture into types more or less their own. In France, for example, occurred several consequent styles: that of the Francis I period, of the Henrys, of the Louis', and, ultimately, of the Empire. In England there was the architecture of the Elizabethan period, the Jacobean, the Christopher Wren, and the William and Mary; and these styles were followed by those of Queen Anne and the Georges. The Colonial work in America stems directly from the Georgian period in England; it is a descendant of the Renaissance of Italy.

Until recently the spirit of the Renaissance was at the root of most architectural work. There were sporadic outbursts of revivals of other styles, but few new forms were developed; and whatever the variations employed in the solution of new problems, the basic motives to a large degree reverted to the Classic or the Renaissance.

MODERNISM IN BUILDING CONSTRUCTION

Early in the nineteenth century, the art of building went into a decline that lasted for some seventy-five years; this period is sometimes referred to as the Dark Ages of architecture. However, since the Victorian period there has been a general revival in building construction, and remarkable progress has been made in many countries. This progress has been due largely to the necessary solution of modern problems and to new methods of construction. The development of structural steel and reinforced concrete, both of which came into existence within the last fifty

THE CHILE HOUSE
IN HAMBURG,
GERMANY

Emphasizing Hamburg's importance as a seaport, this office building is shaped like a ship.

Courtesy German
Railroads Information
Office, N. Y

years, made new forms necessary as well as possible. New movements in design have resulted from underlying causes. The requirements of modern commerce resulted in such buildings as the Wertheim store in Berlin, a notable work by the architect Messel, which marks a new era in commercial architecture. Modern industry dictated the designs of industrial buildings in Germany, France, and the United States, and occasioned a new school of talented architects.

Germany led the modern trend. Alfred Messel abandoned architectural traditions that were no longer useful and turned to a new type of work. He was followed by other brilliant builders, among them Ludwig Hoffman, whose work as city architect of Berlin is notable. Olberich, of Darmstadt, and Wilhelm Krauss helped in the blazing of a new architectural trail. In industrial work the Germans made great advances; among the best designers in this field were Peter Behrens and Bruno Paul.

In France there was strict adherence to tradition until quite recent times. But since the World War there has been a radical change in French buildings, with such architects as the Perrets, Le Corbusier, and Lurcat, pioneering.

Domestic, ecclesiastic, and institutional buildings have accounted for the major portion of recent English architecture. Sir Gilbert Scott, Norman Shaw, Belcher, and others led the way. But in the monument field England has achieved little since the days of Wren and Inigo Jones.

Some of the best modern work is to be found in Sweden. Such structures as the Town Hall in Stockholm, by Oestberg, and the Administration Building of the Swedish Match Company, by Tengbom, are outstanding examples of contemporary buildings.

It is still early to pass judgment on the recent work in Russia, but many notable results may be observed. The tendency is toward

THE ARCHITEC-
TURALLY INTER-
ESTING TOWN
HALL OF
STOCKHOLM

Courtesy Swedish Traffic
Association, Stockholm

constructing buildings on a large scale, and this is evidenced not only in their industrial buildings, such as the Cheliabinsk tractor plant, but also in the great, functional apartment houses that are being built in Moscow and other cities. Their buildings reflect, in many ways, the revolutionary reforms that have taken place in all modes of life.

In America, during the latter part of the nineteenth century, H. H. Richardson and Richard H. Hunt were responsible for many of the best buildings. The work of the former includes such structures as the Trinity Church building in Boston, and the Law School at Cambridge. Later came Charles McKim, who was probably the most important architect of the period. Among his works are the Boston Public Library and the Columbia College buildings. McKim was followed by a new school of architects, the leaders of which were Louis Sullivan and his follower, Frank Lloyd

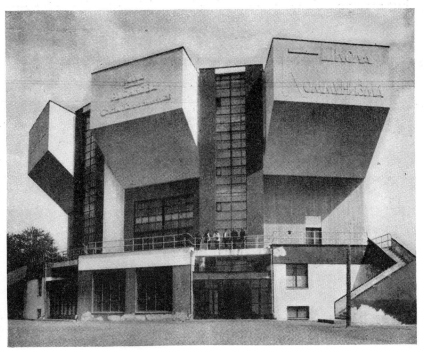

Courtesy The Art Institute of Chicago

A WORKERS' CLUB IN MOSCOW

Intourist photo

ENGINEERS' APARTMENT HOUSE IN MOSCOW

Courtesy and copyright by Boston Public Library Employees Benefit Association

PUBLIC LIBRARY, BOSTON, MASSACHUSETTS
Built by Charles McKim, famous architect of the latter part of the nineteenth century.

Courtesy The Art Institute of Chicago
COURT OF AN ARCHITECT'S HOME
Taliesin, home of Frank Lloyd Wright, at Spring Green, Wisconsin.

Courtesy The Art Institute of Chicago
THE INTERIOR OF A FINE RESIDENCE
The Winslow home in Oak Park, Ill., designed by Frank Lloyd Wright.

Wright. The former, a pioneer in skyscraper construction, was the first architect to make adequate use of the steel-skeleton type of construction which permitted great height in building. The titanic skyscraper was another example of the effect of function upon form; and in the designs Sullivan introduced, the use of steel columns was reflected in the vertical building lines. Wright's work has been more residential than commercial. His functional designs have had considerable effect on building throughout the world; as a matter of fact, his influence abroad has been greater than in his own country. Other American architects, such as Albert Kahn, have made great advances in industrial architecture.

RECENT TRENDS IN RESIDENTIAL STRUCTURES

Today, buildings can be broadly divided into four classes: residential, institutional, commercial, and industrial. The first

FISHER BUILDING
DETROIT,
MICHIGAN

Photo by Drix Duryea,
New York, Courtesy Albert
Kahn, Inc., Architects
and Engineers

class consists of homes, apartments, hotels, clubs, and the like. Institutional buildings comprise schools, hospitals, libraries, museums, churches, and monuments. The third group includes such structures as office buildings, stores, and the modern theaters. In the industrial class are factories, administration buildings, warehouses, and power plants.

In the field of residential architecture, the last few years have seen some radical changes. Many of these changes have been the direct result of functional purpose of modern manufacturing buildings. The Germans, Erich Mendelssohn, Walter Gropius, and Bruno Paul, and the Frenchmen, Le Corbusier and Lurcat, have carried many of the principles of industrial design into non-industrial buildings; their homes, schools, office buildings, and shops reflect the trend in design for which manufacturing demands have been largely responsible. Sometimes this trend has resulted in exaggerations and eccentricities. Modernizing in certain buildings has produced a simplicity frequently reduced to baldness; in Germany this result is called "Rasierte Architectur," or "Shaven Architecture." On the whole, however, the tendency is toward the elimination of superfluous details and the effecting of the greatest conveniences in homes and other such structures. Frank

Courtesy Albert Kahn, Inc., Architects and Engineers

INTERIOR OF FORD ENGINEERING BUILDING, DEARBORN, MICHIGAN

Lloyd Wright has been one of the pioneers in this development. Today the west coast of America offers many examples of the functional tendency in residences.

In comparison with other building developments, the materials used in house construction have undergone little change during the last hundred years. Stone, brick, lumber, sand, and lime today perform purposes similar to those in 1837. The interior conveniences of houses have, of course, considerably improved, but the materials for exterior construction have changed comparatively little. However, there is under consideration a new theory of house construction which, if adopted to any great extent, would revolutionize the building of residences. This theory deals with the prefabrication of houses. This term is almost self-explanatory, and means the factory construction of whole house sections which at a later period are to be assembled for habitation.

Various objections have been raised to house prefabrication, and without question the idea does involve certain serious problems. For example, the execution on a large scale of this method of building houses might disastrously affect different building trades. Such trades will naturally oppose the movement as much as is within their power. Also, there is some question as to the eagerness with which local dealers and contractors will welcome house prefabrication, and perhaps some doubt concerning the extent of their willingness to market and erect such houses. A major consideration, of course, is the manner in which the public will react to a scheme which tends to produce large numbers of almost identical houses and to eliminate to a great extent individual characteristics.

On the other hand, there are important advantages in prefabrication. This manner of construction would make many houses very much cheaper, and consequently available to many people who hitherto have been unable to afford homes. Moreover, alterations in houses would become simpler to handle and far less expensive; with little difficulty houses could be reshaped and changed to meet new demands. In fact, theoretically it would be possible to move houses from one locale to another without great trouble.

Photo by Wesley Bowman Studio

JANE ADDAMS HOUSING PROJECT IN CHICAGO

It is difficult to prophesy at this point the future of house pre-fabrication. Its success or failure will be subject to many conditioning factors, social and economic. However, the probability is that since the movement would be unquestionably a progressive one, it ultimately will take place in one form or another, meeting the various problems as they arise.

Another modern trend is toward the supervision of designing of a large number of houses by governmental agencies. In the United States the national government has shown great interest in the problem of general housing. In England the building of Garden Cities illustrated the British intention of making an increasing number of houses available to the people. It is true that certain objections have been raised to the designing of houses *en masse,* but at the same time, there can be no question that housing plans, if executed efficiently, make comfortable homes obtainable for many families that otherwise could not afford them.

ARCHITECTURAL GIANTS OF COMMERCE

During the past thirty years the greatest development in construction has unquestionably taken place in buildings of the commercial and industrial types. Until the latter part of the nineteenth century, the weight of the floors and roof in multi-storied buildings was carried by the walls. The thickness of these walls increased in the successive stories from the top down to the foundation. The practical and economical limitations of wall thickness naturally limited the number of stories which could be built, and the buildings in the latter part of the nineteenth century were limited to ten stories in height.

With the advent of steel and reinforced concrete as structural materials, it became possible to construct skeleton frames which carried the floor and roof loads previously carried by the walls. Relieved of this function, the thickness of walls could be greatly reduced. Structural steel and reinforced concrete framework made possible the construction of the high buildings of today. In the first years of the twentieth century, buildings reached a height of twenty-five stories; today a structure such as the Empire State Building of New York has over a hundred stories.

The construction of high buildings in large metropolitan areas was found to restrict light and air between adjacent structures, and led to a new design known as the "stepped" or "set-back" type of building. Upper floors were set back at various stages to admit light and air to the street and lower story levels. This "set-back" type was originated by Saarinen, a Finnish architect. His ideas were further and intensively developed by American architects, with the result that the modernistic design of skyscrapers is one of America's contributions to architecture.

BRINGING LIGHT AND UTILITY TO FACTORIES

Probably the most important structural work being done today relates to modern industry; and in no other field, during the last fifty years, has there been such improvement. Yet orderly and studied factory designing is a comparatively recent development. Progress was first made in the factories of the textile industry in New England, where so-called heavy timber construction was adopted. Additional light resulted, because the heavier beams made possible greater window areas; moreover, the beams, because of their thickness and slow-burning qualities, lessened the fire hazard.

Courtesy Albert Kahn, Inc., Architects and Engineers   Photo by Multi-Color, Detroit

ASSEMBLY PLANT OF GENERAL MOTORS AT LINDEN, NEW JERSEY

With the improved type of building provided by the textile industry, interest in factory planning became more general, and more attention was paid to systematic planning and external appearance. In this connection the demands of labor have played an important part. Laborers grew tired of working in unsanitary surroundings, with poor lighting and ventilation. Strikes among textile workers drew attention to the need for improvements, and modern factory design has done much to eliminate the objectionable features of the old buildings.

Heavy timber construction, although a distinct advance, failed to meet many requirements in the manufacture of products other than textiles. Timber floors were detrimentally affected by oils and other liquids used in many processes of manufacture. Column spacings, which rarely exceeded twenty feet, were inadequate for a large number of manufacturing purposes. Masonry piers in multi-story buildings became excessive in size and restricted the glass areas in the exterior walls. In order to secure adequate natural lighting, single-story buildings were rarely more than forty feet wide. As a consequence, the steel skeleton construction was introduced, and the immediate result was the availability of increased glass area, and increased column spacing.

But the steel skeleton construction failed to meet other requirements. It provided a greater fire hazard, because the steel twisted and buckled under heat, and the building might be reduced to a misshapen mass even if it did not burn down. The problem of fireproofing was solved when François Hennibique, a worker, conceived the idea of strengthening concrete by the use of steel rods. This principle of reinforced concrete construction was first adopted on a wide scale in Europe and later came to the United States. Today there is scarcely any limitation to the use of the material.

NEBRASKA STATE CAPITOL, LINCOLN, NEBRASKA

FACTORY DESIGNING

Contemporaneously with the development of reinforced concrete, a new industry came into existence: the manufacture of the automobile. This industry was responsible for many modernizations in buildings for manufacturing. Mass production necessitated structural improvements; and the automobile manufacturers turned to wide, systematic, abundantly lighted factories. There came into being an effective system of plan and design, the result of which is the modern daylight factory. The first example of this type of structure was the Packard Motor Car factory in Detroit, designed in 1903 by Albert Kahn.

The main purpose of a factory building, of course, is to house manufacturing equipment so that production may be accomplished with the greatest possible efficiency and economy. In this connection, there are four general principles which apply to all types of such buildings: First, materials in the course of production should be transported the shortest possible distance and with the least amount of handling. Second, since a straight line is the shortest distance between two points, production should flow in such a line; the raw materials coming in at one end and the finished goods leaving at the other. Third, the production layout should be as simple as possible. Finally, all departments must be properly correlated and provision made for future expansion with the least amount of alteration to existing departments.

Naturally there are many additional considerations in designing factories. Entrances, stairs, and elevators should be located where they are most accessible and where they will least interfere with production. Locker rooms, toilet rooms, and the like, must be located conveniently, and where their use will cause the least amount of lost time. There must be proper ventilation and an abundance of light in the interior. There should be as few internal columns as economic construction will permit. Floor heights must be adapted to the nature of the product and the methods of manufacture. All floors must be strong enough for the work to be performed on them, yet they must not be overly strong or construction costs will become excessive.

The modern factory is strictly a utilitarian building, designed for the specific purpose of manufacturing a particular product. A pin factory has one design, a locomotive plant another. Therefore, before blueprints are made, a plan for the manufacturing of the goods to be produced must be drawn up; the suitable layout for manufacturing equipment must be determined; and finally, the building has to be designed around the equipment in such a way as to permit its most efficient functioning.

Modern factories have proved that the creating of structures for purely utilitarian purposes need by no means eliminate artistic results. True, the primary concern is one of practicality; but the able industrial architect today knows that a factory building, well planned, well lighted and ventilated, and of pleasing appearance, can be built at a cost not exceeding that of a plain, unattractive structure. Moreover, he knows that such a building usually proves the more efficient. However, artistic results are not necessarily achieved through the use of ornamentation, but rather through the correct handling of construction materials, the proper accentuation of mass and voids, and the suitable proportioning of the structure as a whole; and all these factors are

Courtesy Owens-Illinois Glass Company

GLASS BLOCK CONSTRUCTION SUPPLIES DIFFUSED DAYLIGHT
New plant of the American Education Press in Columbus, Ohio, showing how panels of translucent glass blocks were used to supply ample but diffused daylight.

conditioned by the use to which the building is to be put. The fact is that the most efficient designs for factories have generally an architectural value of their own. The achievement of economic and expeditious production is reflected in the simple and direct lines of the industrial building. The functional demands of industry have produced an architectural form.

HOW HIGH AND HOW LOW?

Should a building be one story, or should it be built in layers that finally lose themselves among the clouds? In the case of commercial buildings which must produce the maximum annual yield on the investment, the value and the area of ground available will be deciding factors. Since the annual returns are determined by the usable floor area of the building, it is obvious that costly land must be devoted to multi-storied structures. It is cheaper to build many stories than to spread out over expensive land. On the other hand, the value of the land is of less importance in the case of industrial buildings. The determining factors, always, are what is to be made and how it is to be made, because the annual returns on capital invested depend upon economical and expeditious production. In general it can be said that when the product is of such a nature that it is composed of relatively small parts, for example, typewriters, sewing machines, household appliances and the like, the multi-storied factory will prove of advantage. Elevators are generally used for transporting materials from floor to floor in buildings of this type. Or, if the parts of the product are such that they can be transported from floor to floor by means of conveyors, these are used. On the other hand, if the product or its parts are of a bulky nature, the use of elevators or conveyors would retard production; in such cases the single-story building is preferable.

Industrialists of today are adopting assembly lines extensively in the fabrication of their products. In many cases it is necessary that these assembly lines should be fairly long. For example, the assembly line used in the production of motor cars is approximately eight hundred feet in length. Long, single-storied buildings are then required.

Courtesy Rockefeller Center, N. Y.   Photo by Seidman, N. Y.

ROCKEFELLER CENTER, NEW YORK

Designs of structures in general are not only influenced by the purpose to which the building is to be put, but also by the locality in which the structure is erected. The locality is of importance because the building must be designed to withstand local weather conditions.

A BUILDING'S FEET

Disaster would follow an attempt to erect a heavy building on marshy, sandy soil. The structure would sink and crack, much to the owner's dismay. As many builders have discovered to their sorrow, no structure is stronger than the foundation on which it is built. The type of foundation depends upon the nature of the supporting ground. Where this ground can carry a pressure ranging from two to four tons per square foot, the ordinary type of concrete footings can be used to advantage. Where the soil can support less weight, it is often advantageous to use a spread footing or even a floating raft; such forms of construction distribute the weight of the building over a greater area of ground, and reduce the pressure per square foot to the safe bearing capacity of the soil.

Where the top layers of soil have a low bearing capacity, with firmer soil or rock underneath, piles are often used; in such cases better soil or rock must be found at a depth not more than eighty feet below the surface. If soil suitable for footing is found at a depth of not more than fifty feet, wood piles are used. When the bearing soil is found at a greater depth than fifty feet, concrete or steel piles are used. For foundations supporting very heavy loads, to reach bearing soil or rock at a great depth below the surface level, long concrete caissons are constructed to pierce the earth in order that a building may rise into the sky.

TRANSLUCENT WALLS

Generally, the superstructure of the building has exterior walls which are one of two types—the self-supporting and the supported. The former are used for buildings not more than six stories high. In these cases the walls are designed to carry the load

Courtesy New York Central Lines

SUNLIGHT FLOODS A METROPOLITAN RAILROAD STATION
The New York Central station in New York brilliantly illuminated by nature's own
lighting system, thro igh the architect's arrangement of windows.

of the various floors. In buildings more than six stories high, it proves economical to use a structural framework which carries not only the load of the floors, but also the weight of the walls between the piers. In this type of structure the spandrel, or outside walls will not be as thick as in the case of the heavy supporting walls, because of the extra thickness is of no advantage from a carrying point of view and has the disadvantage of increasing the load to be carried on the structural framework.

The materials used in the construction of the exterior walls will, to a great extent, depend not only upon the locality of the structure, but also upon the character of the building—whether it is to be non-fireproof, slow burning, or fireproof. In the first, the walls will probably be of wood or brick. In the last, the walls will be of brick, stone, or reinforced concrete. A new building material recently has come into use, namely, glass brick. The use

Courtesy Chicago & Northwestern Railway

ARCHITECT'S PANORAMIC VIEW OF THE NORTHWESTERN
STATION IN CHICAGO

of this material makes walls that admit light; but in buildings having glass brick walls, there is no means of securing natural ventilation, consequently such buildings must be provided with mechanical means of ventilation.

Exterior walls in modern buildings are insulated with cork, fibrous vegetable materials, or pressed mineral materials. The outside finish can consist of many different materials, such as face brick, stone, stucco cement, and so forth. Stucco cement is suitable only in warm climates. In cold climates any moisture which finds its way between the stucco finish and the masonry backing, may freeze and cause the stucco to disintegrate.

The interior walls of buildings were formerly constructed of wood and plaster. In modern buildings cinder blocks and pressed

Courtesy Chicago & Northwestern Railway

INTERIOR CROSS SECTION OF STATION

fibrous materials have been extensively used. The interior walls can be finished with plaster, paper, or other materials. Of late there has come into extensive use a material which consists of a very thin layer of wood gummed to paper backing. This is then applied like ordinary wallpaper.

FLOORS MUST BE STRONG

A floor is prosaic, but it must be built with adequate structural strength. Floors of buildings must be designed safely to carry the load that may be put upon them. Those of residences are ordinarily built to carry a weight of forty pounds per square foot. The floors of office buildings are designed to carry a load of eighty pounds per square foot. Industrial building floors carry loads ranging from one hundred to two hundred and fifty pounds per square foot, depending upon the nature of the product turned out and the weight of the equipment required in its manufacture.

The materials used for floor construction depend upon the character of the building. In the ordinary type of residence, wood beams and flooring prove adequate; but in costly residences the floors are generally constructed of fireproof material, such as hollow tile or reinforced concrete. In office buildings, in multi-storied industrial buildings, or in institutional buildings where relatively large crowds congregate, the floors must be of fireproof construction.

Floor finishes likewise vary with the building's purpose. Wood finish is most suitable for residential buildings. The floors of office buildings are finished with wood, marble, tile, or some plastic material, such as Gibraltar or terrazzo finish. Where it can be afforded, the use of wood-block floor is most suitable because it is not costly to repair the damage caused by heavy traffic. In some portions of factory buildings, such as toilet rooms, locker rooms, and the like, Gibraltar or terrazzo finish proves of advantage, since such floors facilitate washing and general cleaning.

COLUMNS

The spacing of interior columns for buildings depends upon the character of the building. In general, it is desirable to have as few internal columns as possible, because these columns obstruct the use of the floor. In multi-storied apartment buildings, hotels, offices, and the like, the interior columns should be spaced about twenty or twenty-five feet apart, because these dimensions are suitable for the spacing of interior walls, in which the interior columns can be imbedded. Increasing the distance between columns increases the cost of construction, and this is another reason why the columns should be relatively close together in buildings of this character.

In the case of industrial buildings, however, the cost of building construction is of less importance than the manufacturing cost of the product. Since interior columns obstruct manufacturing processes, industrial buildings should have as few interior columns as possible; therefore, the distance between columns is greatly increased.

ROOFS MUST NOT FALL

Several years ago patrons of a theater were more than astonished when the roof fell in under the weight of a heavy snowfall. This disaster illustrates clearly the fact that roofs, like floors, must be designed to carry the load they will have to support. The locality of the structure is a governing factor in their design. In northern climates the roofs of buildings must carry the weight of heavy snowfalls. In some localities the depth of snow can cause a load as great as fifty pounds per square foot. In southern climates, where snow loads are of no concern, the roofs will not need to carry more than the weight of heavy rainfalls or heavy wind

Courtesy Northern Pacific Railway

NORTHERN PACIFIC STATION AT HELENA, MONTANA

pressure. In such buildings roofs need to be designed to support superimposed loads of not more than twenty pounds per square foot, in addition to the heavy wind loads.

The materials of which roofs are constructed will depend upon the character of the building. For buildings like residences, wood roofs are serviceable. If the building is of the type which necessitates a fireproof construction, the material used for roofs should be reinforced concrete or structural steel supporting noncombustible roof slabs.

Dripping roofs can cause great discomfort and damage. Various materials can be used for waterproofing the roofs, but here again the type of structure is the governing factor. The wood roofs of residences are covered with wood shingles, slate, plastic or ceramic tile. In institutional buildings, having fireproof roof construction, the waterproofing may consist of felt impregnated with pitch, asphalt, or similar materials.

The roofs of modern buildings are often insulated against heat and cold. The insulating material can consist of cork, fibrous vegetable materials, or compressed mineral substances. The thickness of the insulating material is governed by the degree of insulation desired. In general, it can be said that cork ranging from one inch to two inches in thickness will produce the desired effect. The thickness of other materials will depend upon their relative insulating values.

Since modern industrial buildings cover large areas of ground, the roofs must be designed to admit light to the interior; windows in the external walls of such buildings will not admit enough daylight. There are various means of effecting roof lighting. The principal one lies in the use of monitors with glazed sidewalls. The amount of light to be admitted into the interior of the building is governed by the nature of the product manufactured. The area of glazing in the sidewalls of the monitors will consequently vary from eighteen per cent to thirty per cent of the area of the floor covered by the roof.

THE PROBLEM OF SANITATION

The plumbing in a building involves the piping and fixtures for distribution and use of water, and the drainage pipes and fixtures for carrying away rainwater, waste water, and sewage. It also includes piping to bring water to the building from water mains, as well as the piping to take the sewage from the building to the main sewers.

The arrangement of the plumbing system and the sizes of the pipe used have an important bearing on the consumption of water and the disposal of the waste. If the water distribution throughout the building is well proportioned, the use of water in any one part will not draw water away from fixtures in other parts of the building and decrease the flow. Similarly, the size of waste and soil pipes should be so determined that the danger of clogging drains is minimized.

Water piping is made of lead, copper, brass, iron, or steel. Ferrous pipes are sometimes galvanized to avoid being corroded in course of time. Pipes installed for the purpose of conducting acids or other corroding liquids are lined with lead, rubber, or other noncorrosive materials, especially where these pipes are made of iron or steel.

For many years plumbing fixtures were made of cast iron; but in modern buildings these fixtures are now made of vitreous clay. The latter ones have a much better appearance and have a longer life than the former.

HEATING SYSTEMS

Fireplaces and stoves were never satisfactory methods of conquering cold. In addition to the inconvenience of carrying fuel, these crude devices did not distribute heat where desired. Stoves are obviously unsatisfactory in large structures. The heating of buildings can be accomplished in many ways. In Europe the term "central heating" is often used to mean the supply of heat from a central source in a particular building. In the United States, however, it generally means the supplying of heat to a group of

A MODERN HOME
HEATING PLANT

Courtesy Holland
Furnace Company

buildings from a single heating plant, such as a boiler house. Heat from such a heating plant is conveyed in the form of steam or hot water through properly proportioned pipes.

The advantage of steam over hot water is that it is of a higher temperature, and can be conveyed through smaller sized pipes, the result being a corresponding reduction in cost of installation. In steam systems, however, the condensed steam must be returned to the central heating plant, and this necessitates special fittings which are a source of trouble and inconvenience.

A hot-water system, on the other hand, has advantages over a steam system, which compensate for its slight extra installation cost. Since the temperature of hot water is lower than that of steam, its use results in a more uniformly distributed heat. This uniformity of heat may also achieve a saving in cost of fuel.

The heating of buildings can be accomplished by means of hot air. In the past, hot air was adaptable only to small buildings, such as residences; but with the advent of motor-driven fans, hot air can now be propelled over relatively long distances, and such systems are now installed in buildings of considerable size.

Industrial buildings, covering expansive areas of ground, are economically heated by means of unit heaters distributed throughout the plant. These heaters are merely hot-air units. The heating medium—either steam or hot water—is conveyed from the central heating plant to the various unit heaters. The steam or hot water passes through coils in these heaters, and motor-driven fans blow air over these coils. The air thus warmed is then directed into the room to be heated.

It is economical to install, maintain, and operate a unit heater system. It has a further advantage in that the moving air results in ventilation. There is practically no limit to the size of buildings which can be heated by the unit system.

Air conditioning is a recent development of hot-air heating. The term "air conditioning" means the provision of the proper amount of useful moisture in the air. It is well known that the heating of air results in the apparent removal of the moisture. Hot, dry air has a detrimental effect upon the occupants of a building, and this disadvantage is overcome by adding a certain amount of moisture. This amount must be controlled, because either excessive or insufficient moisture will prove objectionable.

Air cooling is a natural development from air conditioning. Just as air can be warmed by passing over coils containing steam or hot water, it also can be cooled by passing over coils containing a refrigerating fluid. The refrigerant may be obtained from a refrigerating machine, or may be cold water.

VENTILATION

Proper ventilation is a requirement of all modern buildings, and may be either natural or artificial. Natural ventilation results from the opening of windows in exterior walls, or in roof monitors. In the case of industrial buildings the side-wall and monitor windows should be designed so that at least fifty per cent of their area can be opened.

Artificial ventilation is effected by means of motor-driven fans, which may be installed either in combination with, or independent of, the heating system. The fan-driven air is conveyed

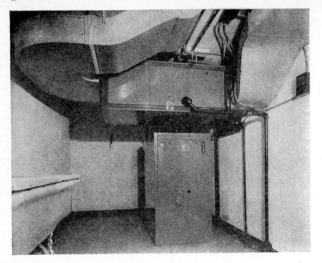

MODERN HOME HEATING AND VENTILATING SYSTEM

Auxiliary type complete conditioning system including house heating oil burning boiler and air conditioning unit suspended from the ceiling.

Courtesy American Radiator Co.
Photo by Drix Duryea, Inc., N. Y.

through ducts. A properly designed ventilating system will not only provide sufficient fresh air, but it will also extract the foul air.

The degree of ventilation is measured by the number of air changes occasioned per hour. For ordinary purposes, four air changes per hour will prove sufficient; but under conditions of closely applied work there should be at least eight changes of air per hour. Excessive rapidity in the changing of air tends to cause drafts and should be avoided.

LIGHTING

Ordinary windows in exterior walls should be as large as possible. The ratio of window area to the solid wall area will vary according to the purpose to which the building is to be put. In residential buildings at least fifteen per cent of the outer wall area should consist of windows. In office buildings the area of the windows should be at least twenty per cent of the total outside wall area. In residential and office buildings it is bad practice to use an excessive number of windows, as they create difficulties in heating and cooling.

In the case of industrial buildings, however, an abundance of light is of advantage in obtaining efficient production. Industrialists find it more economical to waste fuel for heating purposes than to waste labor through insufficient lighting. In industrial buildings the external windows should be not less than forty per cent of the total wall area. In many cases they are as much as seventy-five per cent of the area.

The need for an abundance of daylight was not recognized in the old type of industrial building, and the small windows then used had wood frames. The large window area installed in the modern industrial building necessitates the use of steel window frames. In modern office buildings the window frames are constructed either of steel or some non-ferrous metal such as aluminum or bronze.

The need for effective artificial lighting is probably more pressing than the need for natural lighting, especially in buildings in which work is being performed. Under ordinary circumstances darkness occurs toward the end of the working day, when the worker is subject to fatigue. Poor lighting tends to increase fatigue, diminish efficiency of production, and, in the case of industrial buildings, increase the risk of accident. Much attention is paid today to the subject of artificial lighting.

In residences, apartments, and hotels, the lighting systems are designed to produce an intensity ranging from five to ten foot-candles. In office buildings the intensity will vary from ten to twenty foot-candles; and in industrial buildings the intensity will vary from twenty to eighty foot-candles on the working plane, depending upon the degree of accuracy involved in the work performed. Uniformity of lighting is almost as important as intensity. Variations in the intensity of lighting have a detrimental effect upon the worker. Uniformity of lighting results from the proper location of the lighting sources.

Electric lighting is used in all modern buildings. For many purposes the ordinary filament lamp, having a wide range in lumens or intensity, is suitable. In the original electric lamp, invented by Edison, the filament consisted of a finely-spun carbon element contained in a vacuum. The next development was the Cooper-Hewitt lamp which consisted of a glass tube containing mercury. This lamp proved more efficient than the Edison lamp, but it proved disadvantageous in the color of the light, the com-

Courtesy Owens-Illinois Glass Company

GOING THE CHAMELEON ONE BETTER

Through the use of glass blocks, behind which an arrangement of vari-colored bulbs allows
the building to change color nightly, architects achieved an unusually effective and arresting
sight in this department store building.

plexity of its construction and installation. These disadvantages
have lately been eliminated to a great extent.

The next development of the electric lamp was the substitution of a tungsten wire filament for the original carbon filament,
the tungsten wire proving more effective than the carbon element.
Further development followed by the elimination of the vacuum
and the substitution of gas-filled lamps.

The latest advance in electric lamps is the so-called "high-
intensity" lamp, containing mercury vapor. This vapor is electrically heated to a high temperature. The new type of lamp
embodies all the commendable features of all previous lamps and
overcomes many of their defects.

NEW DEVELOPMENTS

As a consequence of the progress in artificial ventilation, air
conditioning, air cooling, and electric lighting, there has developed
a new building design which has neither windows in the exterior
walls nor roof monitors. There are many proponents of this type
of building; they claim that the saving in its cost of construction
compensates for the increased operating costs due to artificial
lighting and ventilation. They also claim that the artificial, rather

than natural, ventilation and lighting can be more uniformly regulated, resulting in increased efficiency from the occupants of the building. The claims made by the proponents of windowless building are still to be verified; working within blank walls must be reserved until more time has elapsed to obtain experience in their use.

The psychological effect of having to work in a windowless building is still to be determined; working within blank walls may produce in men a sense of prison-like confinement. But when one remembers the numbers of people who live and work in poorly lighted factories, and in mines, this liability may be discounted.

Courtesy Oklahoma City Chamber of Commerce

NIGHT SCENE, CIVIC CENTER, OKLAHOMA CITY, OKLAHOMA

Courtesy U. S. Navy (Official photograph)

AERIAL VIEW OF DOCKS AND PORTION OF THE CITY
OF PENSACOLA, FLORIDA

THE ENGINEERING OF CITIES

HOW CITIES HAVE GROWN

IT MIGHT WELL BE SAID that the major accomplishment of
engineering is the great American city of today. In every
phase of urban life are inextricably woven the steel sinews of
engineering. This complex profession serves the city dweller in
countless ways. The development of engineering knowledge and
skills has made possible the life of millions of people within a relatively small land area. Engineering manifestations are found
throughout the construction of a city—from the simplest grading
of a street to the most complex skyscraper, with its hidden steel
structure and its underground pilings. Bridges, viaducts, power
plants, traction systems, radio towers, airports, harbors, and even
the brilliant electric signs that punctuate the night—all of these
are services and adjuncts of engineering which make for the good
life and the comfort of urban dwellers.

Why are millions of people willing to crowd themselves into
huge metropolitan centers? Why did they leave the open countryside for the congestion of city streets? Urban living conditions
are very different from the rural life to which most city dwellers
were accustomed. When the United States embarked upon its
career as an independent nation, it had not a single town with as
many as 50,000 inhabitants. Not until 1820 could it boast of a
city with over 100,000 people, and not until 1880 did it have a
city of a million. Today the majority of Americans are city dwellers. They live in 3,164 urban places of which five have a population of over a million, and ninety-three exceed 100,000. We must
stop and consider carefully the importance of this statement.
Only five per cent of the American people used to live in cities.
That figure has now grown to about 56 per cent.

By 1930 there were nearly fifteen times as many people living
on farms in the United States as there were in 1790; but there
were more than 300 times as many people living in cities. The
proportion of farmers has been decreasing very rapidly during

Courtesy Canadian Travel Bureau, Ottawa

OTTAWA, ONTARIO, CANADA, AT NIGHT

this period. In 1870, 52.8 per cent of American workers were employed in various agricultural pursuits. Today that percentage has fallen to less than 21 per cent. This shift of the population to urban areas carries with it a fundamental change in the entire life of the nation. It means that in little more than a century our country has profoundly altered its mode of life, and has been transformed from a rural society into a full-fledged urban industrial society.

A group of the nation's outstanding political scientists, economists, and educators presented in 1937 the results of a thorough study of the American city. They showed definitely how the city has become a workshop of American civilization. There were more than 3,000 counties in the United States in 1929, but the largest industrial cities were concentrated in only 155 of them. These cities contained more than half of all industrial establishments, and about three-fourths of all industrial wage earners. The products of their factories accounted for about 80 per cent of the value of manufactured goods. This concentration of factories means not only the collection of workers in such areas, but also the existence of large staffs of salaried officers and employees. The majority of wholesaling establishments exist near the factories.

Transportation and communication facilities converge upon the cities. They serve as centers for diffusion of the techniques characteristic of modern civilization. Railroads are arteries running between cities. About three-fourths of all railway traffic terminates in urban areas. There are more than 500 freight stations within thirty-five miles of New York alone. Until recent years consumption of electric energy was confined almost entirely to urban centers. In fact, because of the huge aggregations of people in cities, many of the technical advancements made in the last century find their greatest fruition in such communities.

MEN WHO LIVE IN CITIES

We must briefly consider the man who lives in the city of today, for it is he who is the primary cause of our problems—not as an individual, of course, but when he congregates with his fellow beings in large numbers to engage in a multitude of activities known as "living." It has been said that the city dweller shuttles back and forth from a place where he would rather not live to a place where he would rather not work! He may live either in the city or in its suburbs. He works, almost invariably, in the most congested part of the business section. In his daily movement from home to office, of which the clock and time schedule are symbolic, the commuter exhibits the peculiar division between working and living that is characteristic of all urban society. Only a small fraction of people live in the same location as their employment. This is a sharp contrast to the shop of a hundred years ago with its living quarters for the owner and his family. The homes in American cities are to be found as far from the business center as the worker can conveniently locate them. There are to be found blocks after blocks of apartment houses within the city limits. In the suburbs there are rows upon rows of more or less uniform five- and six-room houses. Farther out there are the larger and more pretentious homes of the executives and the wealthier classes.

The suburbanite, in his daily routine, is engaged in a vocation involving the humdrum, high-speed, technical work of business, industry, and the professions. He works in the heart of the metropolis, and finds recreation in an avocation which may range from amateur gardening to politics. He is not an exception to the urban dweller, but merely a variety of his personality. The motives leading to this type of existence are to be sought in the urge to escape the obnoxious aspects of urban life without, at the same time, losing access to its economic and cultural advantages. In this process, the form and the functions of the city are being revolutionized.

The problem of urban congestion arises from a striking phenomenon. As the city spreads its far-flung boundaries, it almost invariably rises at the center. Someone has said, "The larger the city, the taller the buildings!" The skyscraper is the visible sign of this congestion at the central axis of a great population center. As the city fills and empties, the streets and traffic facilities, which

Courtesy Milwaukee Association of Commerce   Photo by Aero-Graphic Corp.

PART OF DOWNTOWN MILWAUKEE FROM THE AIR

were designed for smaller cities and lower buildings, are no longer able to carry the load without friction and delays. There are countless other problems that arise from the daily ebb and flow of the human tides in cities. When business life quickens with the dawn of a new day, electrical energy must be supplied in staggering quantities. Veritable rivers of pure water must be available for use. Restaurants and shops must be ready to meet the demands which are certain to be made upon them.

Having given consideration to the economic structure of the city and the social status of its inhabitants, we shall turn to a more complete treatment of some of the many problems which arise from a combination of these many factors. It is in coordinating the life of a city dweller, both his leisure and business hours, that the highest and finest skills of engineering are called into use.

Courtesy Nashville Chamber of Commerce

DOWNTOWN NASHVILLE (TENN.) FROM THE AIR

CITY CANYONS

To the visitor who is accustomed to wide expanses of fields, meadows, and woods, the great stone canyons of American cities must seem fantastic. In the heart of the metropolis these huge box-like buildings are thrown up against the sky, and only a narrow strip of blue may be seen by those who look above them. The daylight which these buildings shut out is replaced by artificial illumination, the wide expanses of blue sky and white clouds being comparatively unknown to the city dweller. The city is not a natural arrangement, but rather it is artificial, its uniform outlines being the streets that bisect and cut through its countless groups of buildings of varying heights and sizes. Straight lines are works of man, not of nature. These streets and broad highways are the first manifestations of the accuracy of the engineering profession which we encounter when we approach the city. True as a die, and of uniform width, smooth, hard-surfaced super-highways and well-drained streets may be followed from the outskirts of the city into the very heart of the business district, and again to the broad fields beyond. The precision, the sharp lines, the consistency, and the sameness of this man-built structure—the city—are all directly attributed to the painstaking effort, knowledge, and labor of the engineer.

If the observer views the American city from an airplane, it will appear as a sprawling mass of structures of varying size, shape, and construction, criss-crossed by a checkerboard street pattern. Close examination will show that the city is more densely built up at the core, where, though it be only a few square miles in area, one or more tall structures will loom up grotesquely, marking the location of the central business district. If the city is large, the number of these skyscrapers will be correspondingly multiplied and they will reappear irregularly at places somewhat distant from the center of the city, indicating the location of sub-centers. The central business district will flatten out abruptly toward the edges, where the city's light manufacturing and ware-house areas may be recognized, interspersed by ramshackle structures constituting the blighted areas and slums. Adjacent to this belt are to be found the tenements and working men's homes, and beyond are the more densely built apartment house sections, tapering off rather unsymmetrically and stretching finger-like along the main traffic streets into single homes with small yards and open spaces. Along these radials that show the main transportation lines, and like a web between them, are clustered other more or less intensely built up settlements. The city will thus approximate a circular or semi-circular pattern, the edges of which will protrude, tending to stretch the circle into a star-shaped outline.

This is a picture of the great American metropolis, rising at its center as though the buildings were thrown upward by some gigantic force, and stretching to its outskirts in narrow tendrils. From its roadways and its bridges to its sidewalks and curbings, from its tallest tower to its smallest home—into every single piece of construction, planning, and operation has gone the technical knowledge of the engineer. This is indeed a picture of the American city in which every brush stroke has been made by an engineer.

CENTERS OF POPULATION AND BUSINESS

The city, which first developed from the beginning of commerce, has now also become a center of manufacturing. However, commercial and service enterprises have kept pace with manufacturing, as is indicated by the increasing proportion of workers in large cities who are classified as "white collar workers." As industry and population in a city increase, and as larger areas outside of the city are brought within its influence, the demand for services increases. The range of occupations, incomes, and consequently standards of living, tends to increase with the size of the city, producing greater diversity and contrasts between various sections of the city and its population. This tremendous increase in the population of our cities and the multiplication of functions have increased manyfold the problems of the engineer. Once he concerned himself principally with the building of structures which would house the looms and machines of industry. Today he must provide clean, light, and harmoniously attractive space for business men of all sorts, for professional groups and countless commercial activities which demand the finest in office accommodations. Former residence sections felt the effects of expanding business when rows of houses were torn down to be replaced by modern office buildings and factories.

It is little short of amazing that half a million people must crowd themselves into an area about a half-mile square—pile themselves on top of each other, row on row, to engage in businesses and activities from which they gain their livelihood. To the farmer who plows his fields, it is scarcely believable that anything can be important enough to make myriads of people jam themselves into an area smaller than his cornfield.

It is the centralization of business—the facility with which it can be transacted when men are in close contact with its many associated component parts—that makes them crowd themselves together. Since it is not possible for many people to occupy the

Courtesy Canadian Travel Bureau

PART OF TORONTO'S SKYLINE
The Royal York Hotel, Toronto, Ontario, and surroundings.

same space on the ground, that area has been multiplied many times by erecting buildings of many stories, thus gaining an amazing amount of additional room. In some congested centers the land area has been multiplied as many as twenty-five times to accommodate the needs of the population. The skyscraper of to-day will house as many as a thousand people on one city lot two hundred and fifty feet by four hundred feet—a space smaller than the average barnyard.

It is obvious that such a piece of ground possesses an enormous value in terms of money. An acre of his land may be worth eighty dollars to a farmer, but a like amount of land would be worth many thousands of dollars if it were in a city where countless people could avail themselves of it.

CLOUD SCRATCHERS AND SKYSCRAPERS

In a surprisingly brief period of time, American engineering has aided in converting villages into towns and towns into great cities. Log cabins were replaced by frame houses, and they in turn

Courtesy Los Angeles County Chamber of Commerce

THE NEW CITY HALL IN LOS ANGELES

by brick houses. The increase in population demanded that residence facilities become more concentrated, which resulted in multi-storied apartment houses and hotels. Eight- and ten-story office buildings, considered by the last generation as being just about the last word, have been torn down to be replaced by colossal skyscrapers. Cobblestone and wood-block roads have been replaced by asphalt and concrete. Single-track car lines have given way to double tracks, and these have been replaced in some instances by busses. The explanation of this unprecedented rate of obsolescence and rebuilding lies partly in the rapid growth and spread of population which swiftly overtaxed and overloaded existing facilities. We discard that which we do not use and replace it by the newest and most modern thing which does its task with the best dispatch—whether it be an automobile or a drawbridge.

A short time ago men were wondering at the skill and great ability of engineers who designed the Woolworth Building in New York. They said it was the eighth wonder of the world; but engineers have since designed and built three skyscrapers that have pushed it into comparative obscurity. They are the R. C. A. Building, the Chrysler Building, and the Empire State Building which rears its majestic head a quarter of a mile into the sky. The floor space of Chicago's thirty-six-story Merchandise Mart is of such an area that the three and one-half million inhabitants of that city could be accommodated in the building, if each could stand on one square foot of space. In Los Angeles a striking new Municipal Building boasts a tower of white stone; an arresting sight against California's intense blue sky.

As long as there is need and use for tall buildings, the engineer can plan and construct them. We must not for a moment think that the profession has exhausted the possibilities of building tall structures. They can be as easily built to nearly twice the height of today, but the demand has not yet become apparent. It is not the desire to amaze people that prompts the engineer to raise buildings high above the ground, but rather the demand of business that prompts the exercise of the knowledge and skill which go into the building of a skyscraper.

XIV—15

Photo by Chicago Architectural Photographing Co.
A STRIKING VIEW IN A MAN-MADE CANYON
LaSalle Street, Chicago, with the Board of Trade Building in the background.

ERECTING A SKYSCRAPER

The problem of providing quarters in one building for enough people to form a small town is not a simple one. Its solution requires a diversity of knowledge of building in its many component parts. It is the acid test of the engineer. The foundations of such a building must be sunk deep into the ground; they must be on a firm foundation—on bedrock, if that is possible. These huge blocks of cement and steel upon which the walls of the building will rest, are constructed to withstand a maximum of weight that may be placed upon them, not only the weight of the building itself, but also of the people who will tread the floors and add many thousands of pounds additional strain. This is one of the most important tasks of the engineer: calculating the strength of materials and estimating the weight that will be applied to them. Inside the stone walls of the modern building of today is a framework of steel, riveted into place and providing a skeleton upon which is hung the form of stone, windows, floors, and other covering. The engineer must consider the building materials which are most suited from many different viewpoints. Weather conditions may determine that only certain kinds of material may be used. Fire hazards are the greatest limitation.

Space within the building must be planned. There must be adequate halls for the movement of the inhabitants. Each room must have access to fresh air. Space cannot be wasted; a maximum of utility must be gained. The various floor areas must be divided and subdivided to accommodate each particular business and to make for utmost convenience. Once we have provided space for hundreds of people, the problem of transporting them to that space commands attention and requires utmost skill.

VERTICAL TRANSPORTATION

One of the most exacting of all tasks of the engineer is the planning, construction, and operation schedule of elevators. The man on the thirty-ninth story of a building cannot be expected to climb up to his office in the morning and descend to the ground

PASSENGER
ELEVATORS IN
A MODERN
DEPARTMENT
STORE

Courtesy Marshall
Field & Company

each evening. In the course of the day he may travel up and down many times. Nor can he spend many of his precious minutes being raised or lowered in a slow-moving elevator. He must be whisked quickly, safely, and silently to his office in a fraction of a minute. The problem is further complicated by the fact that most of the occupants of a single building will arrive at approximately the same time each morning and will leave at the same time each evening. The demand is met by the engineer, who devises the system by which the people who occupy the building may be moved in the least amount of time. To do this, he may design elevators which carry a greater number of people, or, perhaps, draw plans for high-speed elevators that are intended to carry persons to and from the higher levels of the building.

To pursue the same problem a step further, the engineer must determine the most practical size of the elevator. Structural difficulties prevent him from making an elevator car as large as a room, even if so large a car were desirable. A large unit would have further difficulties of attaining speed; it would have to have more power per person than does a smaller car, since the larger unit builds up a greater air pressure in the shaft. The speed of the elevator, likewise, must not be too great for comfort; so the engineer chooses equipment which will make possible the most comfortable ride. Modern elevators are so skilfully constructed and operated that riders are scarcely conscious of movement.

SAFETY FROM FIRE

Nor is the engineer concerned merely with problems that concern the bringing of people to their offices and making them comfortable. He must protect them from the danger of fire. Years ago, when buildings were usually constructed of wood, fire was an ever present hazard. Hot summer months dried out the wood of the building, making it a tinder that could burst into flame when ignited, or, as was often the case, the wood might begin to burn by the process of spontaneous combustion.

The great Chicago fire of 1871 was an example of fire razing a city built of wood. The center of that great city was burned to the ground in a fire that lasted several days. The wood structures of Chicago burned with such intensity that even the iron nails and spikes of a hardware store were fused into a solid mass. The intense heat cracked the stones of buildings and bricks, ordinarily fireproof, became plastic.

Engineers knew that the best way of preventing the recurrence of such a holocaust was to minimize the use of inflammable materials in the construction of city buildings. Thus Chicago, which had been a city of wood houses, was rebuilt as a city of stone, brick, and steel.

Today numerous precautions are taken to prevent the spread of a fire in crowded areas of cities. In addition to an increased use of stone and brick in building construction, provisions have been made for isolating fires in parts of buildings by building fireproof partitions. Floors and walls are made of concrete; large steel doors can be closed on whole sections of buildings, keeping the fire in a single great vault out of which it cannot escape. Window casings and doorways, formerly made of wood, are now usually made of steel. Plaster walls are now on a base of steel netting, where formerly they had been on a base of wooden laths. Even such office equipment as desks, cabinets, and chairs are made of metals. Electric wires, which once were strung in networks throughout the walls of buildings, are now encased in pipes of metal, reducing the hazard of crossed wires. No detail in modern construction escapes the engineer in his effort to keep the human inhabitants of his buildings safe from fire.

Older buildings, not fully fireproof, are made safer by putting in pipes to which fire hoses can be attached at a moment's notice. Steel fire escapes are securely fastened to the outside walls of buildings to give avenues of safety to persons who might not be able to leave buildings by other means when fires break out. Special fire alarms have been invented which instantly turn on a torrent of water when the temperature of a room rises above 150° Fahrenheit. These sprinklers, usually seen suspended from the ceilings of the rooms of large buildings, are controlled by a metal fuse which melts when a room becomes abnormally warm.

The engineer is winning the battle with fire. We can look forward to the day when the battle may be won.

HEAT, LIGHT, WATER, AND POWER

Not only must the engineer concern himself with providing the space within the heart of the city, but he must also exercise his skill in providing services for those buildings. A high degree of specialized knowledge is required to design a radiation system which will draw steam or hot water from a central heating unit and distribute it safely throughout every room and hall in a large building. This heat must be conducted through walls, floors, in and out of rooms, and must be spread economically as well as adequately throughout the building to give uniform heat to all areas.

A maximum amount of daylight must be provided in each room, and artificial light must be available on the slightest notice.

An overcast sky, a sudden storm, will send countless light switches clicking during the middle of the day in offices where work is being done. Uniform light is a necessity to safeguard the eyes of office workers.

The water supply of a modern office building is one of the engineer's chief problems of providing convenience. The system must be so designed that water can be pumped to taps in the penthouse as easily as to those on the ground floor. The engineer also lays out his water system so that all parts of the building are furnished with an adequate supply and pressure. This is especially important in regard to fire protection. Hydrants are placed at strategic points throughout the entire building, and a length of neatly folded fire hose is attached to each hydrant, ready for instant use.

The skyscraper of today supplies an enormous amount of power to those who work within its walls. In a modern office building there are countless adding machines and other pieces of

Courtesy York Ice Machinery Corp., York, Penna.

EFFICIENCY AND DIGNITY MARK THIS BANKING OFFICE

commercial office equipment which require electric current for their operation. There are machines for light manufacturing in office buildings; there may be small printing presses; and there may even be steam-driven equipment. Each of these constitutes a new set of problems for the engineer. In the economy of time and space which modern business has developed, the drawing of water, the lighting of lamps, and the turning of wheels must be done for us if we are to gain the maximum returns from the amount of time we spend. It is an age of specialization, and the engineer must expend his every effort to do those things for man which will leave him free to engage in other pursuits—whether they be for business or pleasure.

CONVENIENCE IN CITIES

The daily bringing together of many people into a small area to work and to engage in activity which furthers the process of living means that countless other services must be available to those people. Many things must be done for them which they would otherwise take time to do for themselves. The office worker usually buys his lunch. He purchases his clothes, and most of the items needed for his daily life, within a short distance of the place where he works. The woman in the family, who is employed in an office or a store, does her shopping on her way home after the day's work is done. As a consequence, countless businesses and services locate as near the center of commerce and business as they possibly can. They cater to the people who daily pass their doors. These extra activities of the city worker complicate the tasks of the engineer.

A great population center, which is also a center of commerce, service, and industry, draws to it countless people from other cities and from outlying territory, and, indeed, from other countries. These people have as their main purpose the transaction of certain business. They require housing that is convenient to the place where they must do that business. And so in the midst of office buildings, department stores, and manufacturing plants, we find hotels, restaurants, and all manner of enterprises which make readily available every attribute of modern life. Within one

EXACT METHODS FEATURE MODERN OFFICE PRACTICE

LUXURIOUS SURROUNDINGS FOR THE DINER-OUT

Rich and graceful decorations in modernistic style feature this dining room in Central Terminal, Buffalo. Wainscoting is of black and gold marble, and dining alcoves are hidden by glass and ornamental iron screens.

Courtesy Swedish Traffic Association, Stockholm
MODERN RESIDENTIAL APARTMENTS IN STOCKHOLM, SWEDEN

building a person may eat, sleep, buy almost anything, get his hair cut, have his laundry done and his clothing pressed, attend the theater, dance at a night club, and enjoy most of the conveniences which in a smaller community would be lodged in a dozen different establishments. Again the engineer is called upon to make these many different services available in a limited area.

Nor are the problems of the engineer confined, by any means, to providing housing for business and the construction of skyscrapers in the centers of cities. It is just as important that homes be provided for these countless workers. The construction of a five-room cottage, while it requires engineering skill, does not demand as much as the building of a huge apartment house, for the urban dwellers in large numbers live within the outside walls of the same structure. The Marshall Field Garden Apartments in Chicago house seven hundred and fifty families totaling twenty-two hundred people—more than the entire population of many small cities! Many of the same problems are pertinent to housing people in office or home. Varying degrees of skill and application of the same principles are found, of course. It is the problem of the engineer to transform the land area that provides the best available home sites into adequate homes for the city dwellers.

KEEPING A CITY HEALTHFUL

Not the least important problem confronting the city dweller is that of his health. A body acclimated to fresh air and sunshine requires special attention when it is brought into different surroundings, artificial heat, artificial light, and impure air. It is no wonder, then, that the urban resident sometimes pauses to reflect on how his physical being can "take the punishment" that city life inflicts upon it.

The sanitary engineer has come to assume a role equally as important as the construction engineer who is responsible for the building of a city. Without proper sanitation and health-preserving facilities, the people of urban communities would not long survive.

Courtesy Bureau of Engineers, City of Chicago   Photo Chicago Architectural Photographing Co.

THE CRIB AT LINCOLN PARK, CHICAGO

HALL OF SCIENCE BUILDING AT THE CENTURY OF PROGRESS
EXHIBITION, CHICAGO (Designed by Paul Cret.)

The sanitation engineer is largely responsible for the vast decrease in periodic epidemics that result from water-borne disease carriers. The two great advancements in this field have been the scientific purification of a city's water supply, and a thorough treatment of all sewage disposal. In other words, the water supply is controlled from its source to the consumer's tap, and the sewage is controlled from the consumer's drain to the final stage of treatment, the effluent outlet to a stream that carries it away.

The ventilation engineer assists in civic health promotion through his efforts in the installation of modern air-conditioning systems that are to be found in many public buildings and places of importance, such as office buildings, hotels, restaurants, and theaters. This movement is spreading to the individual home, thus providing a more livable atmosphere throughout the day.

Noise and strain have taken their toll among city people to a great extent and in a variety of ways. Noise abatement campaigns have been proposed and carried on with some success. Vehicles and other appurtenances necessary to city life have been engineered to operate in a quieter manner in an effort to reduce the tremendous din that was formerly looked upon as a necessary evil.

The city engineer has also taken a hand in the design of recreational facilities for the urban dwellers. He has provided parks and playground space, public stadiums, public golf courses, airports, swimming pools, bridle paths, zoos, and boating facilities.

Consequently, when we view our life activities as a whole, and those of cities in particular, it is difficult to find any part or feature that may not be credited, at least in part, to the engineer.

SANITATION

Modern sanitation is a necessity of the modern city. Life for large masses of people partially removed from, and yet closely dependent upon, a constant supply of water, food, fuel, and raw materials, is in itself conditioned by a high degree of technological development and the perfection of administrative organization.

If we recall that many populous oriental countries are frequently afflicted by epidemics that sweep away a large portion of their inhabitants, we can realize the significance of modern sanitation for urban existence. The provision of pure water, of centralized sewage and waste disposal systems, the assurance of a safe food supply, and the prevention and control of contagious diseases, are the chief measures that for more than a century have made it possible for most Western cities to maintain their population by lowering the death rate.

The greatest development of engineering in the field of sanitation has been the modern sewage disposal plant. Since the first rudely constructed sewers of three hundred years ago, cities have disposed of their waste products by emptying them into nearby streams. As the lands adjoining cities have been built up, the flow of impure water from larger adjoining cities has created a public health problem.

Courtesy Metropolitan Water District of Southern California
THE METROPOLITAN AQUEDUCT FROM THE COLORADO RIVER
Each section of the precast concrete pipeline is 12 feet long, 12 feet in diameter, and weighs 42 tons.

Courtesy Bureau of Engineering, City of Chicago   Photo by Peter Fish

PART OF A METROPOLITAN FILTRATION PLANT

The engineer was faced with the necessity of correcting this condition, because the responsibility for it does not rest with the person through whose land the impure water flows; rather it rests with the person living farther up-stream. Consequently, one city that lies up the river from another must make provisions for such treatment of discharged wastes as will eliminate the possibilities of polluting the water of the stream. The sanitary engineer solved this problem by introducing the sewage disposal plant which provides for the treatment of all residential and industrial waste products. Modern engineering science has rendered this process so thorough that the water released from a sewage disposal plant to a river rivals and sometimes betters the quality of that which is taken in to be treated for city consumption.

A MODERN SANITATION PROJECT

A brief consideration of the way in which one metropolitan city has met the problem of sanitation, and called into play many supplementary activities, is worthy of attention. The Chicago

Courtesy Bureau of Engineering, City of Chicago   Peter Fish photo

CHLORINE STORAGE ROOM AT CERMAK PUMP STATION, CHICAGO
The ton container is in position to be lowered into a caustic soda tank in case of serious leakage of chlorine.

Sanitary District was organized in 1889, and its principal object was to render Chicago's water supply clean by keeping its sewage out of Lake Michigan. This was accomplished by building a main channel from the Lake to the Des Plaines River, reversing the flow of the Chicago River and diverting the sewage down the Illinois River to the Mississippi. The North Branch of the Chicago River and the Calumet River had also to be included within the drainage scheme since they also drained sections of Chicago. Consequently, two collateral channels, the North Shore and the Calumet Sag canal, were built. To make the main and collateral channels effective, a network of intercepting sewers and pumping stations was constructed to serve numerous sections and municipalities within the Chicago Sanitary District.

To this elaborate construction program there was added a system of sewage treatment. The original plan called for the conveyance of all sewage to the canals and dilution with sufficient lake water to render it reasonably harmless. With the growth of

Courtesy the Link-Belt Company
OLD METHOD OF CLEANING BAR SCREENS IN A SEWAGE TREATMENT PLANT
Modern engineering has consigned this disagreeable hand operation to obsolescence through the use of straight-line mechanically cleaned screens.
XIV—16

EXCAVATING FOR AN INTERCEPTING SEWER
The steel lining is for temporary support, inside of which is built a concrete lining
three feet thick.

population and industry in Chicago and its suburbs, it soon became evident that dilution had to be supplemented with sewage treatment. Consequently the Chicago Sanitary District's engineers were forced to design methods for the treatment of at least part of the sewage that was being carried through its elaborate channels, sewers, and pumping stations. A program that will also include the treatment of industrial wastes is now in the process of development.

But the Chicago organization has gone far beyond the sanitation problem. It has a hand in the shipping and navigation problem as well. As one of the links in the Mississippi Waterway, now in the course of development, docks and terminals built along its right-of-way form an intimate part of the Lakes-to-Gulf navigation project.

The District's sewage program has necessarily included the construction of locks and dams in the southwestern part of the region at Lockport, in Will County, Illinois. In order to facilitate

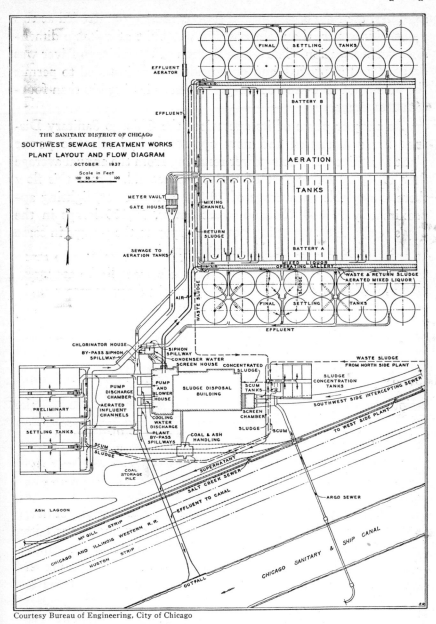

THE SANITARY DISTRICT OF CHICAGO
SOUTHWEST SEWAGE TREATMENT WORKS
PLANT LAYOUT AND FLOW DIAGRAM
OCTOBER 1937
Scale in Feet
100 50 0   100

Courtesy Bureau of Engineering, City of Chicago

DIAGRAM SHOWING PLAN OF SEWAGE TREATMENT WORKS, CHICAGO

shipping, the flow of water and sewage must be controlled at this point. Moreover, the main channel was built of suitable dimensions for navigation. The South Branch of the Chicago River was dredged and improved, and drawbridges were installed to permit the passage of lake- and ocean-going vessels having less than fourteen feet draft.

As another phase of its operation, the Chicago Sanitary District has constructed and now operates a hydroelectric power plant to utilize the water power resulting from the annual average flow of 6,700 cubic feet of water per second. From this flow there is available an average of 20,000 horse-power, lighting approximately 93,000 Chicago street lamps, 30,000 lamps in the city's parks, and furnishing power to operate the pumps in some of the sewage treatment works and pumping stations.

DIRT, SMOKE, AND WASTE

Dirt, smoke, and waste are themselves enemies of public health, as are the polluting effects of industrial and urban waste. In spite of the valiant efforts to enforce smoke abatement ordinances, the belching chimneys of factories, office buildings, and apartment houses fill the air with smoke. This pollution is injurious to the respiratory organs and is forcing people to take refuge in air-conditioned buildings. Soot and grime settle on buildings, dirt blackens the streets, and dust sifts into the homes.

Garbage, considering the size of the task, is generally well disposed of, but sometimes piles up in alleys with obnoxious, if not unhealthful, consequences. One of a few misplaced industries, emitting objectionable odors at times, pollute the air of large sections of the city. Cities, communities, and industries often dump their wastes untreated into the source of water supply. Where regulation and legal powers are not adequate to prevent this, or where conflicting state, county, or city boundaries encourage it, drinking water must be so highly treated with purifying agents as to make it nearly unpalatable. Many bodies of water have also been rendered unfit for sorely needed recreational purposes because the degree of pollution makes their use dangerous.

Courtesy Bureau of Engineering, City of Chicago   Copyright by Chicago Aerial Survey Co.

THE CHICAGO DRAINAGE CANAL SYSTEM

Courtesy Akron Chamber of Commerce

A SECTION OF DOWNTOWN AKRON, "RUBBER CAPITAL"
The Goodrich plant is in the center.

Homer Smith photo, Chicago

FACTORIES IN TAMPERE, FINLAND, "THE SMOKELESS CITY"

Mills and manufacturing plants in this industrial Finnish city are driven by water power.

NOISE AND STRAIN

The large city, especially its central business district, is so characteristically a place of noise that a sudden spell of silence frequently startles the urbanite, for he is accustomed to distracting sounds of all kinds. Screeching trolley cars, lumbering trucks, rasping auto horns, scolding traffic whistles, rumbling elevated trains, staccato pneumatic hammers, open cut-outs, advertising sounds, and air-craft with radio amplifiers—all these, when added together, constitute a din for which it would be impossible to find a precedent in the history of cities. Anti-noise campaigns have been instituted in some of our larger cities, notably New York. Municipalities are also endeavoring to check the din through suitable legislation in the hopes that nerve-racking strains may be eliminated. The city engineer is being assisted in this work by other engineers who are responsible for the design of street cars, for example. Cars of new design have been built and put into operation in an effort to reduce the surface railway's

Courtesy Memphis Chamber of Commerce

MAIN STREET, MEMPHIS, TENN., LOOKING NORTH

contribution to the din. The principal features of construction are lighter weight, producing less impact force, and the use of rubber in the wheels and truck assemblies.

In general, the problem of city noises has not received a great deal of official attention in the past; but the engineers whose labors contribute to the activities of a metropolitan community, are studying to see how they may reduce the irritating noises that are incidental to city life.

PURE WATER FOR THE CONSUMER

The problem of providing pure water for the urbanite is an insistent engineering problem. The attention of construction and chemical engineers must be given to the complex problem of bringing pure water to the city area, and then distributing it into individual dwellings. The fact that the city dweller expects pure water from his tap, pays for it, and so organizes his life, trusting in the purity of that water, is a great challenge to the many men who are charged with the responsibility of furnishing the water.

The water which the city dweller drinks may come from a point one hundred miles away, through a series of syphons, aque-

Courtesy Metropolitan Water District of Southern California
PART OF THE METROPOLITAN AQUEDUCT FROM THE COLORADO
Concrete lined canal which is a part of the aqueduct. The canal is 55 feet wide at the top, 20 feet at the bottom, and 12 feet deep. The aqueduct has a capacity of one thousand million gallons of water daily.

ducts, water mains, and pipe lines, all of which are the developments of the engineer. In New York City the most remote reservoir is one hundred twenty-five miles from the heart of the metropolis. The city of San Francisco, through its Hetch-Hetchy development program, gathers water from the slopes high in the Sierra Nevada mountains.

The water which we drink goes through a series of changes from the time it strikes the earth as rain or snow. It is stored in huge reservoirs from which it is drawn into filtration plants. In these purifying stations it may be sprayed into the air in a process known as aeration, whereby the water sprayed into tiny particles receives the purging effects of both sunlight and pure air. It may be filtered through a series of beds of sand and charcoal. To the water may be added certain chemicals which minimize the bacteria and other unhealthful substances. The water is then sent into the mains through which it is brought to the cities, and carried through pumping plants which give it the necessary power to climb many stories in the pipes that serve the topmost floors of the modern skyscraper.

RECREATION

The city engineer is required to administer to the recreational needs of the city dweller, as well as to provide facilities that make it possible for him to earn his living. Many programs and projects are designed for this specific purpose. Some are more spectacular than others, and an effort is made to provide for the varied interests of a large number of people. All kinds of recreational activities may well be divided into two classes: the first, in which the public assumes the role of spectators, and the second, which features direct participation on the part of the people.

Elaborate zoölogical parks, commonly known as zoos, have been designed and built for the housing and exhibition of rare animals, or at least animals that city people know only from pictures, stories, or hearsay. It is easy to see that features must be incorporated in the design of a zoo that will afford maximum protection to spectators and still allow the animals to

Courtesy Los Angeles Chamber of Commerce

LOS ANGELES MEMORIAL COLISEUM
This bowl has a capacity of 105,000 persons.

Photo by Chicago Architectural Photographing Co.

MUSEUM OF SCIENCE AND INDUSTRY IN CHICAGO

In this new type of museum the principles of science, engineering and industry are portrayed by full-sized and scale-model machines in operation.

be viewed at reasonably close range. Steel-barred cages are the chief means by which this end is attained, but a very interesting departure from this idea is illustrated in the design of the Brookfield Zoo near Chicago. There animals are not placed in barred cages, but are allowed to roam at will in certain sections that very closely resemble their natural habitat. Spectators are afforded protection through the use of deep moats that surround the animals' wandering grounds. The older Lincoln Park Zoo is still retained by the city of Chicago for those who find it inconvenient to visit the zoölogical gardens in suburban Brookfield, some fifteen miles west of the heart of the city. The Central Park Zoo in New York City, and the Zoölogical Gardens in St. Louis are other famous municipal zoos.

Municipal stadiums of impressive size and capacity are also the boast of many of our larger cities. These are provided for the staging of important athletic contests and other exhibitions. This practice dates back to Roman Empire days, as evidenced by the famous Colosseum in Rome that still stands, although in partial ruin. It had a seating capacity of 85,000 persons, about two-thirds of that of the modern Soldier's Field in Chicago which seats 120,000 people.

A very interesting, though rare, type of civic recreational entertainment is the planetarium, of which there are very few in this country. This is a building with a dome-shaped roof. The ceiling is used to represent the overhead canopy of sky. A very complicated, astronomical projection machine throws tiny spots of light on the vaulted ceiling, which represent all the stars in the sky in their relative positions. It is possible to reproduce the arrangement of the heavenly bodies as they appeared on any date in the past, or will appear at any date in the future.

The artistically and scientifically inclined portion of a city's population has not been forgotten by the engineer. He has aided in providing for their recreation and further enlightenment by the construction of buildings for art institutes, museums of natural history, and museums of science. Provision is thus offered for the exhibition of priceless art treasures and invaluable data and specimens of a historic and scientific nature.

Music lovers have received their share of attention in the design and construction of acoustically ideal band shells, from which they may hear the celebrities of the music world playing and singing internationally famous works of the masters. The Hollywood Bowl in California is a fine example of this type of civic recreation work.

Courtesy Chicago Park District

A CONCERT IN THE BAND SHELL, GRANT PARK, CHICAGO
The Chicago Philharmonic Orchestra playing.

Elaborate aquariums have been built by engineers to display in a most efficient manner the numerous varieties of fish, many of which the average city dweller never heard of or saw before in his life. Two of the most famous aquariums in the United States are the one in New York's Battery Park, and the Shedd Aquarium in Chicago's Grant Park.

Perhaps the most complex engineering that is required in the provision of civic recreational facilities, is the exposition. Examples of these projects include Chicago's Columbian Exposition of 1893 and the Century of Progress Exhibiton, the Texas Centennial Exposition, and the Cleveland Exposition of 1936-37. These were exhibitions on a large scale, and included everything from the weight-guessing concession to the exhibit of actual automobile manufacture. Nearly every form of entertainment and educational feature is incorporated into exhibitions of this size,

Courtesy Chicago Park District

AIR VIEW OF JACKSON PARK IN CHICAGO

Courtesy Chicago Park District

A BEAUTY SPOT IN HOLLYWOOD PARK, CHICAGO

which are usually sponsored by private industries and governments, both domestic and foreign.

The activities that are provided for the direct participation of
the public in general are on a less grand scale, but serve a purpose
equally as worthy. Parks and golf courses are the chief facilities
provided, and especially in parks the city planning engineer has
designed activities at which leisure time may be spent.

Playgrounds for children are assuming an increasing importance, largely because of the concentration of buildings on all
available ground space, and also because of the tremendous volumes of dangerous traffic in congested areas. Therefore, steps have
to be taken to provide playing sites for children, since they no
longer have access to an appreciable amount of yard space. Public swimming pools are built to give as many people as possible
the opportunity for water sports, even though they live far from
natural bodies of water.

Boating enthusiasts are provided with harbors, particularly in
cities that are equipped with sizable navigation facilities. These

Courtesy New York Central Lines
MULTIPLE UNIT SUBURBAN TRAIN ENTERING NEW YORK CITY

accommodations are primarily for the larger type of craft, such as motor-powered boats or sailing boats. Many parks, in addition, have artificial lagoons that make possible rowing and canoeing.

MOVEMENT OF MEN AND GOODS

The two great factors which underlie all of the problems which confront the engineer of today when he deals with traffic are mobility and speed. The term traffic includes not only movement of men and goods in automobiles, its most common use, but it includes the general, larger sphere of movement of men and goods by all means of transportation. The urban population of the United States is almost entirely a mobile one. This means that people move about the city as a part of their daily routine or their actual occupation. The great dispatch with which modern business is transacted is due generally to the speed with which transportation is available. Both men and goods can and do move fast in the present age. The problems arising from traffic are the most complicated engineering problems arising out of the concentration of population.

In a study and analysis of the movement of men and goods, the human equation must be considered in its most changeable form. Every day men move to offices distant from their dwelling places. Of this we are certain. We may be fairly certain also that they will require transportation each morning and each evening. But their demand for transportation may vary; there will be times when there will be extra demands on the transportation facilities; there will be periods of unusually heavy shipping. Then, too, there are certain factors which cannot be estimated accurately. It is these unknown quantities that make the task of the engineer more complicated.

THE MORNING AND EVENING RUSH

The first practical problem met by the engineer when he considers traffic is the daily transportation of a large part of the population from the residential sections to the center of business. This working population must be brought into the city in the morning and taken home each evening. Rapid and safe transportation is necessary. Indeed, some of the population may come into the city from a distance of fifty miles—commuters, they

Courtesy Chicago Motor Coach Company

MODERN FULLY ENCLOSED TYPE OF MOTOR COACH

are called. Still further demand is made upon transportation systems by the fact that practically all the employed population moves to and from the center of business at the same time of day. There is a peak load between eight and nine o'clock in the morning and a similar peak load between the hours of five and six each evening. The jostling hundreds who jam the street cars, trains, busses, and elevated lines each morning will be seen on those same trains, eight hours later, engaged in a frantic race to get back to the locality they quit eight hours earlier. At about ten o'clock in the morning there begins another rush as shoppers start for the business district, returning between three and four in the afternoon.

The engineering problems which arise from these peakload periods are many. Equipment must be built that will stand the maximum load. Movement of trains and cars must be spaced for safety as well as for efficiency of operation. It is a strange and challenging paradox that transportation facilities must be most efficient at the most crowded and difficult period of the day.

TRANSIT FACILITIES

One of the primary necessities of urban industry and urban living is a set of rapid transit facilities which connect the various parts of the city with the metropolitan area. These lines bear the brunt of daily movement of the population. The earliest transit facilities were the creations of free private enterprise and were inspired by the profit motive. Thus, transit companies sought franchises, built their lines and made extensions only where they could foresee financial returns. A cardinal principle was that the transit users must be brought to the very heart of the city. This meant that transit lines were constructed to the heart of the community and radiated from the city's center along established and well-traveled thoroughfares.

Population crowding was temporarily relieved by making it possible for workers employed in the center of the city to ignore walking distance in the choice of their residences. Instead, people tended to concentrate within easy walking distance of transit routes. The initial relief from residential congestion near the heart of the city made possible by fast transit facilities was soon counterbalanced by the congestion of traffic itself. New York, Boston, and Chicago resorted to elevated and underground transit systems to relieve the crowding of street traffic caused by the introduction of the automobile.

THE STREETCAR AND CITY TRAFFIC

The time spent in traveling between home and the business center has promoted the development of business in shopping sub-centers and has decreased the utility of the passenger motorcar in the larger cities. In those cities where the streetcar is still in wide use, engineers have found it necessary to re-route cars, to lay new tracks, and to connect the city by creating cross-town lines. In smaller cities the use of privately-owned automobiles has almost entirely replaced the streetcar. In the largest cities traffic hazards, delays, difficulties in parking cars, and the cost of garaging has almost prohibited the use of private cars for daily transportation

Courtesy New Orleans Chamber of Commerce

NEW ORLEANS' FAMED STREET OF TERRAZZO MARBLE
Canal Street, with modern New Orleans on the left and the old city on the right. Brilliantly illumined with more than a million candle power, this five and one-half mile thoroughfare was rebuilt in 1928 at a cost of $3,500,000.

to and from the city. Many people who drive their own automobiles expedite their daily transportation by using the interurban transportation in large centers.

The engineer must concern himself not only with the construction of the transit lines, the cars, and the motors which generate the power for the operation of the system. He is just as vitally interested in the movement of the equipment and its actual operation. It is in this phase of transportation that the engineer finds himself face to face with the uncertain human equation. He must determine the flow of traffic, and carefully study his peak-load data. He must cope with any changes in business or residential areas, since new subdivisions must also be provided with transit facilities. When a public place such as a theater, an amusement park, or a bathing beach is opened, the engineer must make swift adjustments in the operation of the transit facilities that serve the area. He must be prepared to accommodate the equipment to unusual demands. A parade, a football game, a visiting convention, or any occasion which lends itself to crowds will create new problems. Nor can the traffic engineer take his time about studying these problems and working out a carefully planned program. He must act quickly and decisively. He must anticipate every situation which might arise and be prepared to handle it on a moment's notice. There must be, above all, flexibility in the use of the equipment.

AUTOMOBILES

The most significant factor affecting the transportation system of the nation in recent years is the automobile. Motor transportation has diminished the importance of small villages along the railways and has even decreased the importance of intermediate towns as trade centers by making larger cities accessible to greater areas. Within the metropolitan centers the automobile has given impetus to the development of imposing residential suburban cities. Interurban traffic on rails has practically disappeared except for commutation between the central city and its suburbs. It is the greatest factor in transportation within the city limits today.

Courtesy Birmingham Chamber of Commerce
ALABAMA POWER COMPANY BUILDING IN BIRMINGHAM
Called by a London, England, newspaper "one of the three most beautiful power
company buildings in the world."

The coming of the automobile has complicated the economic and social life in this country in nearly every phase. It has created new conditions for the engineer on every hand. It has certainly given him some of his most difficult problems to solve. Street traffic is one of the most important of all the phases of transportation with which the engineer deals today. Those who drive automobiles know that a single stalled car may back up traffic to a depth of two or three city blocks. A raised drawbridge will cause traffic congestion which may take ten or fifteen minutes for the most adroit policeman to untangle. A parade, a fire, or any unusual occurrence which sends people scurrying either in curiosity or for safety will create emergency situations. Any event that brings the ever-curious public together in unreasonable or unusual numbers and causes a flow of traffic at an unnatural rate brings about situations which demand immediate attention.

To better regulate the usual flow of traffic along the city streets, the signal light has been developed. These mechanical devices for controlling the flow of cars are by no means perfect but they do much to keep it under some form of order and afford some protection. The traffic light aims to expedite traffic by being a guide and policeman for motorists; a time saver, and a check on accidents. It is one element in the great system of controls which it is necessary to set up.

MONUMENTS OF THE MOTOR AGE

There are outstanding monuments of the great motor transportation age in every large city today. Stretching across the Golden Gate is a new bridge—the world's longest span—which is a startling tribute to the use of automobiles. In New York there is the great Tri-Borough Bridge. Chicago has almost completed its famous Outer Drive which stretches for more than forty miles along the shores of Lake Michigan. Although it is the main channel of north and south traffic to the "Loop," the addition of an alternate route over the new Link Bridge makes it unnecessary for through north and south traffic to travel the already congested downtown district.

A brief summary of some of the salient features of New York City's most congested area is enlightening. It is one of the most complicated in the country. On the 5,251 miles of streets 790,000 registered motor vehicles move daily, with approximately four to five hundred thousand more visiting motor cars. Around Times Square there are more than two hundred major amusement places with a seating capacity of 200,000. The Grand Central Zone with a daily population of over 300,000 persons, the Queensboro Bridge where 100,000 vehicles have been tabulated in one day, and the Holland Tunnel approaches with more than 50,000 vehicles daily, all make the traffic problem extremely complex.

RAILROADS AND FREIGHT

The city dweller who lives at home and moves into the heart of the city, confining his activities to two small spheres, the one where he lives and the one where he works, is not greatly concerned by the problems of railroad facilities. However, realization that nearly all his food, clothing, furniture, and household necessities must be transported by railroad, truck, or other means, indicates the gigantic extent of this problem.

Courtesy Rock Island Lines

FREIGHT YARDS OF THE ROCK ISLAND AT SILVIS, ILLINOIS

The movement of freight, although not an apparent problem, is one of the greatest in cities today. It exacts severe demands of the engineer in providing mechanical devices suitable for quick handling of ton after ton of merchandise. The problem is further complicated by the added time element in the movement of goods. Foodstuffs for a million people require many cars to a train. Once ample provision has been made to get these goods into the cities, a new problem is to get them there quickly so that daily meals may be as fresh as those of the farmer who has but to go to his kitchen garden for a head of lettuce and to the hen house for freshly laid eggs.

THE RAILROAD AND THE CITY

Just as transportation has been instrumental in shaping the life pattern of urbanites, so it has left its imprint upon the internal structure of the cities. The European cities were already formed when the railroad age dawned in America. The railroad sys-

Courtesy Delaware and Lackawanna Railroad

THE HOBOKEN, N. J., TERMINAL OF THE LACKAWANNA LINES

tem spread before our cities had fully matured, and the newer cities have often been built around the railroad as a center. While new methods of transportation have made possible unprecedented urban development, the replanning of our cities has not taken account of the new mobility.

Our transportation system affects the internal structure of the city largely through the need for terminal facilities, railroad and switching yards, sidings, docks, and wharves, passenger stations, and unloading devices. It is an established fact that yard and terminal costs constitute 54% of the total freight operating expenses. Until recently, terminals were located as closely as possible to the center of the city. The automobile and other facilities for inter-city transportation have helped to reverse this trend. Underlying the multiplication of terminal facilities has been the competitive system under which the railroads and their terminal facilities developed. Most railroad-owned freight houses are operated by and are for the sole use of the railway owning them. Thus in Memphis half a dozen freight houses adjoin each other. In San Francisco three adjoining freight houses were erected as late as 1934. While during most of the transportation history of the United States competition has been a deciding factor in terminal location, in recent years Government regulation and economic necessity have begun to influence terminal consolidation: shifts in location to cheaper land, co-operation among transportation agencies, and modifications in operating methods such as straight delivery and pick-up service, and the use of the freight container.

At present, individual railroads are consolidating stations and other facilities and abandoning those which are the least efficient. Where competition is not too keen, two or more railroads operate joint freight stations. In several cities a terminal operating company controls all switching movements and may operate both freight houses and track yards. In some cities, certain parts of freight terminal operation have been consolidated and "reciprocal switching" is practiced. Pick-up and delivery service is coming constantly into wider use. This is likely to prove exceedingly important in the future for the consolidation and re-location of

Courtesy Elwell Parker Electric Co.

MOTORIZED TRUCK-TRAINS NOW HANDLE BAGGAGE
AT THE LARGER TERMINALS

terminals, inasmuch as freight terminals will find it no longer
necessary to operate in the downtown section of the city, close
to business.

The development of forwarding companies which operate
consolidated terminals is significant. Many cities located on water
have provided municipal water-rail terminals, although for many
years the railroads refused to make use of such terminals. Since
the network of railroads is now well established, it is not likely
that many new roads will be constructed. It is probable, therefore, that the number of railroad terminals is more likely to be
reduced through consolidation and abandonment than increased,
even though certain cities may increase in size.

AIRPLANES AND TRUCKS

Two new additions to the transportation system of the
country have done much to reshape the movement of men and
goods. They are the airplane and the freight truck.

At present the main sphere of the airplane is still passenger
and mail transport, and it serves only the larger urban com-

munities which, in most instances, realize the need of facilitating air traffic by constructing municipal airports. In 1934 there were 702 municipal airports in the United States and 618 commercial ones. By 1936 the number of municipal airports had grown to approximately 750.

In only a very few cities has the problem of air and rail terminal co-ordination been attacked intelligently. The Newark terminal is probably outstanding in this respect. Philadelphia is planning an even more extensive combination rail-waterway-airway-motor terminal on Hogg Island. Chicago is enlarging its present airport to accommodate the new sky-liners that require more landing space. Improvements in the transportation facilities needed to reach the field are also being considered.

In the larger metropolitan districts the freight motor vehicle, the truck, is exerting an important influence upon our transportation system, especially the railroads. As in the case of railroads, the question of motor trucking and bus terminal facilities is important. Motor trucking terminals operated jointly are found in many cities, among them Los Angeles, Chicago, Lincoln, Sioux City, Indianapolis, and Seattle. On the other hand, many cities have a large number of truck terminals. Cincinnati, for example, has thirty-five. While railroads have not been anxious to consolidate their freight terminals, they have frequently pooled their passenger depots into one large station; likewise, joint bus terminals have been established in a number of cities.

THE CO-ORDINATION OF TRAFFIC

It is in the combining of the transportation facilities of the urban community that the engineer must be most skillful. When one or more kinds of transportation overlap, he must deal equitably with both, and must handle problems which are increasingly complex. In the movement of street traffic he must meet problems that concern both trucks and passenger cars. He must provide safety devices to protect automobiles against rushing trains. He must protect the pedestrian and provide him with ample opportunity to cross streets, and move about on foot with safety. The freight terminal and railroad switching yards must bring

KANSAS CITY, MO., FROM THE AIR

Looking northwest across main business section toward the municipal airport, and across the Missouri River, Fairfax Airport (commercial). At left is the Municipal Auditorium, and at right the new Jackson county courthouse with the city hall immediately behind it.

AIR VIEW OF TERMINAL MARKET, LOS ANGELES

freight into the heart of the city without interfering with the movement of regular daily street traffic.

It is quite probable therefore, that in the field of traffic we will see the greatest development of engineering in the years to come; for the world is becoming increasingly smaller as travel from one point to another becomes more rapid. The faster man can move, the more often he will move. Already there are great elevated highways within the larger cities of today. It is the engineer who must give his complete and wide knowledge to increasing the rate and facility of motion of men and goods and at the same time making them safer.

CITIES OF YESTERDAY

The tiny settlements of the Pilgrims along the eastern seacoast were not the first rudiments of cities to be built in the land that is today America. Various civilizations of Cliff Dwellers lived in cities in the west and southwest several hundred years ago. These short, swarthy early Americans built their cities along the canon walls of the Rocky Mountains. The Mesa Verde National Park, in Colorado, contains the largest visible remains of the dwellings of this now extinct race. The Cliff Dwellers lived in apartment houses arranged very much like those of today. They had a central cistern and water supply. There were even rudely constructed sewers. The Cliff Dweller "engineers" were aware of many of the problems which face modern engineers and they applied some of the same solutions to them.

In their crude and primitive way the Pueblo Indians in the southwest also built their houses together and formed compact little cities. Even today there are tribes of these Indians living in the same adobe huts that were built hundreds of years ago by their ancestors. At Taos, New Mexico, 300 Indians live in one large pueblo, honeycombed with rooms. No one knows how many years it has been standing, although some estimate it at nearly a thousand years. These Pueblo Indians learned to use native materials in their buildings, their bricks being made of adobe or mud into which had been mixed straw for binding. These large bricks were laid and then the walls plastered with the same adobe mud, knitting the entire structure together to form a

Courtesy Buffalo Museum of Science

SIOUX INDIANS TRANSPORTING LOADS BY HORSE AND DOG

substantial building. Even the roofs were thatched with adobe and straw. The thick walls afford ample protection against cold in winter and provide a cool interior in the heat of summer.

LIFE IN THE OLD CITIES OF EUROPE

The European cities of yesterday form a shocking contrast to the modern city of today. We are apt to attach too much glamour and romance to the days of the past and to forget that life was lived without the benefit of most of our conveniences. The "Little Old London" of two hundred years ago was a city of very dirty and unkempt streets. There was very little paving. In wet weather carriages were often mired in the mud and travel was almost impossible. Indeed the courteousness of letting the lady walk on the inside of the sidewalk originated in the days of splashing mud from passing wagons and carriages.

Courtesy Buffalo Museum of Science

SIOUX WOMAN (FOREGROUND) WEAVING A BLANKET

It appears logical to assume that lack of engineering skill and genius accounted to some extent for conditions in older European cities that seem appalling to the present generation of people. Health preservation and transportation facilities were given very little thought in past generations. Only very recently an organized and skilled engineering profession has wrought significant changes in the mode of living.

Sanitation was a dreadful and most unpleasant problem before the days of the modern sewer system. Many houses dumped their refuse into the gutters along the street. It has been told that one of the bishops of London carried an orange with him when he went into certain sections of the city,—"that he might sniff it, so oppressive was the odor upon the streets!" What a welcome thing a heavy rain must have been to the dwellers in crowded, unpleasant cities in those days.

A PAPAGO INDIAN WOOD CARRIER

THE HOGAN—LOGS, EARTH-COVERED
(Southwestern United States)

CITIES OF THE FAR EAST

In the Far East and in the Orient there have been cities of great size for many hundreds of years. Even today these cities form a strange contrast to the modern American city. Although Western ways are gradually being adopted, we may still see camels in daily use for transportation of men and goods. The elephant is still actively engaged in his age-old occupations of dragging, carrying, and lifting in the East. In the cities of the hot climate there are standing today buildings that have done service for many hundreds of years. The white walls which reflect the intense heat rays of the sun are much the same as they were in biblical times.

THE OLD AND THE NEW

And so the story goes—we find many cities loath to change from the old ways of living and doing things, and we find others a strange mixture of old-world architecture and clanging modern streetcars. Electricity has wrought miracles in some of these age-old centers of population. Brilliantly-lighted signs glitter across the yellow roofs of Peking, and an airplane beacon flashes out from the top of the Eiffel tower piercing the night sky of Paris with stabbing streaks of dazzling light. Modern streamlined architecture has found its place alongside the old, tiled roofs of Stockholm. Everywhere there is the automobile and its silent counterpart, the traffic light.

Thus does the transformation of the ancient cities of the world typify the spirit of the modern age. The stately beauty and chiseled grace of the old Greek cities, the noble columns and monuments that adorned ancient Rome, the sweeping Gothic grandeur of the medieval town, all these shall be cherished among the great achievements of the race. To the moderns there remains the problem of retaining in the cities of the future the beauty that glorified the cities of the past, at the same time eliminating the disease and discomfort experienced by those who dwelt in them. With a broad vision of both beauty and utility we may yet hope to see the "alabaster city, undimmed by human tears."

CENTRAL BUSINESS DISTRICT OF DALLAS, TEXAS

CITIES OF TOMORROW

The engineers who must build the cities of tomorrow—and who indeed are already well on their way—face new problems, but with a firm, solid background of experience upon which to draw. The science of engineering has advanced so rapidly and so far that it is able to cope more scientifically with the problems which arise daily in this increasingly complicated life. More is known of building materials; the knowledge of electrical power and energy is adequate for years to come. We have learned much about the movements of men and the tendencies and trends of business within the cities. Travel has been speeded up, and responds to control in a remarkable way.

The engineer and architect have injected into the new buildings of today refreshing styles of design that foreshadow the buildings of tomorrow. The set-back architecture of the modern

Courtesy Owens-Illinois Glass Company

POETRY IN STRUCTURAL MATERIALS

New type "rounded architecture," combining brick, concrete and the newly developed glass blocks. The building is the new warehouse of the Hecht Company in Washington, D. C.

Courtesy City Press Headquarters, Atlantic City, N. J.

CONVENTION HALL AT ATLANTIC CITY, NEW JERSEY
The hall seats 60,000, and can be converted into a football field, skating rink, or other
sport arena, with comparatively little effort.

sky-scraper strikes the new note. Simple lines and great masses
have proved the most pleasing to the eye in the construction of
huge buildings. Glass brick is being used in ways which take
advantage of its double utility—as a structural material and one
which permits daylight to pass through the walls of a building!
Engineers are resorting more and more to the use of metal—
principally steel—not only as a "back-bone" for the modern
building, but also as a decorative material and for use in furniture.

Our highways, bridges, and city streets are being constructed
with an eye to the ever increasing speed which the future fore-
tells. The cities of tomorrow will be bisected not only on the
ground level, but on several levels above by wide super-highways. The ground itself will become increasingly honeycombed
with subway and rapid transit lines.

The city of tomorrow will also be a safer place to live in
than the city of today. Not only has medical science made great
strides in prolonging the life span of man, but the engineer has

done much to eliminate dangers which lurk in the everyday world. His skill is protecting life and property more completely each year. There has been, for several years, an alarming increase in the death rate from accidents. To curb this toll, the engineer has introduced many new devices and firm measures have been taken to protect lives of citizens. Grade separations have been built at dangerous railroad crossings, and in large cities there are pedestrian passageways under the dangerous traffic of busy streets.

THE ENGINEER AND LEISURE TIME

More and more we are having done for us mechanically the things which consume time and energy. Our periods of leisure are being extended from year to year. Some of this time is being put to further occupational use, but the greater part of it is being used by the city dweller solely for leisure. With the increased amount of recreational time there are countless new problems for the city engineer to solve. He will be called on to design more parks, more playgrounds, more athletic fields and more picnic areas in the cities of tomorrow. Many of the city dwellers will move farther into the country surrounding the metropolitan area and will commute on high-speed trains. They will engage in more pastoral pursuits for recreation and leisure over the long week ends that will be theirs when it takes them but thirty hours a week to dispose of their vocational responsibilities.

PLANNING

The huge, streamlined air-conditioned cities of tomorrow will not grow up over night. If they are to be the convenient, safe, and delightful places to live in that we wish them to be, systematic planning and skilful engineering will be required. We will have to marshal all the facts, techniques, and knowledge of the past. The engineer will play an increasingly important part in the building of these cities. Responsibility for the mechanics of the urban life of the future will rest on his profession.

Land use is the first problem that presents itself to the engineers. There must be no costly mistakes in erecting the huge skyscrapers of tomorrow; we must conserve our energies and our

Paul's Photos, Chicago

A CITY PLANNED FOR THE MOTOR AGE

Air view of a section of Radburn, N. J., showing closed-end streets opening on traffic avenues, with parks and walks in the center of super-blocks.

resources. Relocation of business areas into newer ones where expansion and development is possible, may necessitate changes in city transportation systems. As traffic and population increase, wider streets must be built. We must have swift and safe highways that provide easy egress from the center of the city.

PLANNING A SAFER CITY LIFE

The physician, the public health officer, and the engineer must join together in a mighty effort to eradicate the dangers to health from the cities. More and better sewage disposal plants will be erected in all large cities; and waste will be more completely treated, no longer constituting a virulent jeopardy to the health of a whole community. Smoke from industrial plants and residential areas will be abated, and the air that we breathe will be purified and cleansed in most public places and in countless homes. The city of tomorrow will be free from most of the menaces to public health that were prevalent in nearly every city of ten years ago.

New and finer provisions will be found for recreation. We will not be forced to take refuge in motion picture houses during hot weather. Out of doors will once more play a greater part. The man who is released from his office during daylight hours will enjoy himself in the parks and natural areas that are set aside for him. Life will be greatly enriched in countless other ways.

Through all of the visioning of the cities of tomorrow there is a definite challenge. In all that is attempted toward development of urban areas, planning must be foremost. There must be no hasty or ill-advised steps, for each new undertaking, whether it be a commercial venture of a one-hundred-story sky-scraper, or whether it be an artificial lake in an underprivileged area, must be a part of a long-range plan to derive the maximum benefit from the use of the land and the outlay of capital.

Aggressive cities the world over are already meeting the needs of modern urban life. New York with its elevated highways, Chicago with its sewage disposal system, Los Angeles with its water system, and numerous other cities are but previews of the future day when life in an urban center will be free from the disadvantages it knows today. New problems will always arise—but with the memory of past achievement the engineer can face the future with confidence.

Courtesy Chicago Park District

BELMONT HARBOR, LINCOLN PARK, CHICAGO

TVA POWER TRANSMISSION LINE AT WILSON DAM

THE ENGINEERING OF POWER

MAN AND POWER

THE ONE THING, above all others, that the swift pace of modern civilizations depends on is *power*—power in large quantities. Without it the great roar of industry, the security we possess against nature's inconveniences, the extraordinary speed with which we travel across continents and over oceans would all be impossible.

Centuries ago man did not have at his command the power he has today. It is available to him in almost countless forms and enables him to perform everyday tasks, the sight of which would probably paralyze members of former generations. The necessities, conveniences, and comforts that man has put at his own disposal, have come about only because he has power available in huge quantities, and the knowledge of how to make it do his bidding. Even until comparatively recent years, man did not dream of super ocean liners, one-hundred-mile-an-hour trains, ocean-spanning airplanes, and the universality of electricity, to mention merely a few of the modern achievements with which we are all so familiar.

Industry has assumed a completely new aspect with the advent of great quantities of power in usable form. Huge factories avail themselves of this power to turn out better products at a lower cost, thereby benefiting more people. Industry has changed drastically from the old guild days when practically everything was produced by hand. At the present time, even a small factory can produce more in a week than the craftsman might in his entire lifetime.

Man has always needed power to do even the simplest and lightest of tasks. His first requirement—back in prehistoric ages—was probably the power necessary to move things from one place to another. If the objects were not too heavy, for example,

Courtesy Buffalo Museum of Science

MODEL OF THE FIRST WHEELS WITH FIXED AXLES
Some genius of the far-distant past found that disks cut from large logs and fastened on axles would transport heavy loads with greater facility than the sled, and so wheeled transportation was born.

the larger animals he killed for his food, he moved them by dragging them along behind him. Later, he determined to move bigger things, some of which were not easily dragged, and one method he employed was to place them on simple carrying devices equipped with runners, which eased his burden somewhat. When he reached the limitations of this means of transportation, he was sufficiently advanced in knowledge to fashion a rough wheel, and this is undoubtedly how the lowly cart had its origin.

MULTIPLYING MUSCLES—THE LEVER

Later, by putting a shaft through a wheel and a handle near the outer rim, man found he could raise objects by winding a rope around the shaft and attaching the other end of the rope to the object to be lifted. This simple machine was the forerunner of many lifting devices, which, although their construction and operation may be more complicated, have as their fundamental principle this process of turning a crank and thereby winding a rope around a shaft. This device, which persists even to the present day, is used in lifting the bucket from a water well. The shaft passes horizontally between two upright supports on the rim of the well, has a crank on one end, and the lifting rope is wound around the shaft. The reason for putting the crank handle near the rim of the wheel is to make it easier to revolve the shaft. It would be very difficult, if not impossible, to turn the shaft itself directly; so the crank is installed to give "leverage" and make rotation possible.

Courtesy Buffalo Museum of Science

MODEL SHOWING USE OF SIMPLE PULLEY AGAINST ITS MODERN COUNTERPART IN BACKGROUND

The lever was among the first implements known to man whereby he could apply power to any object in excess of his own muscular capabilities. Archimedes, in the third century B.C., was acquainted with the law of the lever in its simplest form. This fundamental knowledge was elaborated by Leonardo da Vinci in the fifteenth century.

When Archimedes discovered the fundamentals of the lever, he hit upon what seemed to him a startling fact. He claimed that, because of the leverage principle, he could lift the world if he had a lever of sufficient length! At one time or another, we have seen a heavy rock moved or lifted by resting a crowbar over another rock, slipping one end of the bar under the rock, and pushing down on the other end. This is the principle of the lever.

The oar of a boat is another adaptation of the lever. Ancient galleons, some of considerable size, were propelled by great numbers of oars manned by slaves. The stones comprising the ancient pyramids of Egypt were shifted about from place to place by means of levers.

A familiar and picturesque illustration of the lever is the handle of the old farm pump. The early printing presses were operated by turning a lever in a horizontal arc around a geared upright bar. This action pressed the type against the paper with enough force to make the impression.

A modern illustration of the lever with which most of us are familiar is the jack of an automobile. We know that it would take a very exceptional person to lift the end of an automobile by muscular effort alone; but the leverage, or increase in lifting power, that is obtained through the jack handle, makes it possible for almost anyone to perform that difficult task with ease.

PRIMITIVE TOOLS

The wedge, too, is a primitive tool found in both ancient and modern civilizations. A solid metal wedge can split a log of wood lengthwise with but just a few sharp blows applied to the blunt end. The first wedges were rather crudely fashioned out of stones by ancient people. The stone was chipped until it assumed a shape with one sharp end and one blunt end. This was achieved by tapering the sides from the blunt end where the force is applied down to the point. In more recent times, wedges have been shaped from various durable metals.

The pulley is a mechanical device common in everyday life. Like the lever and wedge, it is a machine for the duplication and re-duplication of the intensity of a force. A peg projecting horizontally from a wall with a rope passed over it is essentially a

MODEL OF EARLY APPLICATION OF POWER BY THE USE OF A CAPSTAN

Courtesy Buffalo Museum of Science

Courtesy Buffalo Museum of Science

SPLITTING LOG BY MEANS OF
FIXED WEDGE

Courtesy Buffalo Museum of Science

PRIMITIVE MAN MOVING HUGE
STONE WITH WEDGES

Courtesy Buffalo Museum of Science

MODEL SHOWING PRINCIPLE OF ARCHIMEDES' SCREW
A spiral conduit around an inclined axis raises liquids by rotation.

Courtesy Ingersoll-Rand Company

AIR MOTOR HOIST WITH
TOP HOOK

pulley. A tree limb with a rope suspended over it illustrates the same principle. However, a wheel with a grooved rim is more desirable because the friction is diminished. In 1610, Stevin, a Dutch mathematician, formulated the principle of action of the pulley, basing it on the fact that a rope is of an equal tension at all points along its length.

Modern pulleys have become, in some cases, very complex in design and operation. There is practically no limit to the number of pulley wheels that may be included in a single pulley system. A system called the "differential pulley," consisting of two pulleys of different diameters and one rope around both wheels, will give a power ratio of as high as one to sixty; that is, a one-pound pull on the rope will exert a sixty-pound pull on the object to be lifted. Belt wheels, used in power transmission, are often referred to as pulleys.

THE BEGINNINGS OF HORSEPOWER

As man became more intelligent, he sought to make his life more comfortable and profitable. However, some of his tasks required power which was beyond his ability to supply through his own efforts. It was then that he turned to the problem of capturing and domesticating animals that possessed superior physical power.

The origin of animal domestication for labor purposes is rather vague, but over a period of many years, the horse, ox, ass, mule, water buffalo, elephant, camel, dog, and reindeer have been put in service, mostly for the purpose of transporting man or his possessions. Later, animals were used to help till the soil by dragging plows. This practice has persisted even to the present day, despite the great strides that have been achieved in mechanical power implements. Today, in India for example, a remarkable contrast may be observed when one notes a team of oxen pulling its load on the road alongside a modern motor vehicle.

The power of animals has been further exploited by coupling them with simple machines to make even more power possible. This may be illustrated by a device still used on farms to raise hay from a wagon to the hayloft. Three pulleys are used in the setup: one over the wagon at the center of the roof of the barn; the second at the same elevation but at the outside end of the barn; and the third at a point directly below the second. A rope through all these pulleys has one end attached to the horse's harness, the other end to the implement lifting the hay from the wagon. The horse, in walking away from the third pulley, pulls the rope, thus raising the hay from the wagon in the barn to the loft, where a carrier attachment will take the hay to any part of the barn's length for storage.

The use of the lever is coupled with the power of an animal in a simple water wheel. The animal, by walking in circles, actuates a mechanism that lifts water for irrigation or other purposes.

THE OLD MILLSTREAM

Water, like fire, is a most useful servant and a most terrible master. Early in his history, man knew very little about the possibilities of water and its power, using it only for its life-giving qualities, and as a means of transportation. Eventually, however, man learned that water falling from a height possessed power. This power of falling water is referred to as the "head," or the measure of stored-up force, a quality which is also associated with moving streams. One of the earliest utilizations of water power was the old millstream.

Mills were equipped with a large wheel, rotated by means of its paddles, which dipped below the surface of the water and were pushed by the moving stream. This is the "undershot" type of water wheel. The "overshot" wheel is operated by a stream that

CROSS SECTION
OF A 54,000 H.P.
TURBINE
Compare the figure of
the engineer standing
on platform in upper
part of picture.

Courtesy Allis-Chalmers
Company

meets the wheel at its topmost point and falls into buckets on the rim of the wheel. The weight and impact of the water on the buckets rotate the wheel, and the water spills out into another channel at the bottom of the wheel.

The first problem concerning the water wheel was to make it work; after this was accomplished, the problem changed to that of increasing its efficiency. The first wheels were of uniform size and were placed in the stream regardless of the channel's width; hence a great amount of potential power flowed by without coming in contact with the paddles. Later on, however, flumes were built just wide enough to accommodate the paddles. All of the water had to go through the flume and thus strike the paddles as it went by. This innovation rendered a marked increase in the efficiency of the wheel.

There are small wheels for farm use today that show the result of constant improvements, delivering anywhere from seventy to ninety-two per cent of the power of the stream. One of the largest overshot wheels in existence, located in Laxey on the Isle of

Man, is seventy-two and one-half feet in diameter. The water turbine, although it receives its power from the same source and in much the same manner, differs from the water wheel to some extent. The main difference between a water wheel and a turbine is that the latter rotates horizontally around a vertical shaft and is fed by water under pressure in pipes or through nozzles. The former, as described, rotates vertically around a horizontal shaft and receives power from an open stream.

The most familiar use of the turbine is as a prime mover in a hydroelectric generating plant. The three principal types are: the radial; the axial; and the combined, or mixed, flow. These classifications are descriptive of the manner in which the wheel receives its water.

The speed of a turbine is regulated by the amount of water it is fed through gates and valves. Some improvements of these features include automatic devices to close or open the gates, depending on the loading conditions of the turbine at any particular time. During periods of slack power-requirements, the gates will automatically close to a certain degree, restricting the amount of water being fed to the runners of the turbine.

FROM MILLSTREAM TO BOULDER DAM

Water power was taken advantage of in the United States almost from the time the first colonists set foot on its shores. This was true particularly from Pennsylvania to New England. Mills for almost every imaginable purpose were constructed: flour mills, saw mills, grist mills, paper mills, woolen mills, and a host of others. At first they were of the crudest types, but, as capital and skill increased, larger streams were harnessed with better mills. These better and larger mills were made necessary by an increase in population, but early attempts at utilizing water power seem very insignificant when compared with some of our huge modern developments.

The water turbines installed at Niagara Falls in 1894 and 1895 were the most powerful at that time, but the size, grandeur, and magnificence of some of our modern hydroelectric plants bring

Courtesy Union Pacific Railroad

BOULDER DAM FROM THE AIR
The Nevada spillway is in the foreground, with the one in Arizona in the background.

expressions of awe and wonderment from those who actually see them. It seems that each project is an attempt to outdo the last in magnificence. Three of the greatest dams in the world are Boulder Dam of the Colorado River, Grand Coulee Dam of the Columbia River, and Norris Dam of the Tennessee River. Boulder is the highest in the world—727 feet from its base of bedrock to the highway across its crest. The tremendous power necessary to operate the turbines is made possible by the creation of an artificial lake, 115 miles long, behind the dam. Other purposes of this project are flood control and irrigation.

The passing of recent years has witnessed an ever increasing demand for more power. Periods of prosperity brought about the expansion of many industries, and, while it is true that economic progress has suffered periodic recessions, the general trend of power requirements mounts higher. The demand is met by the construction of new power development projects, and the modernization and increased capacity of existing plants.

The famous Niagara Falls power plant was originally equipped with ten 5,000-horsepower generating units. Today, it has six units, each capable of delivering 37,500 horsepower. The increased activities of eastern manufacturing centers demanded this stepping up of power facilities not only at Niagara, but at other power development sites also. The Caribou plant of the Great Western Power Company in California has in operation Pelton wheels producing 30,000 horsepower.

At the end of the year 1935, it was estimated by the Department of the Interior that the total capacity of water wheels at water-power plants throughout the United States amounted to more than 16,000,000 horsepower. In the year 1921, only about 8,000,000 horsepower was developed. The amount of hydraulic power that is available is a definitely fixed quantity, and as a result the utilization and control of our water-power resources have become great problems.

It has been termed a social as well as an engineering and economic problem to determine a means of conserving and controlling our water-power resources. Our imagination does not have to be stretched unduly to realize what would happen should this important source of power be denied us. The cessation of the

Courtesy Union Pacific Railroad
BIRDSEYE VIEW OF BOULDER DAM FROM THE AIR

electricity generated by water power would be a calamity of national importance. The important sources of water supply, lakes, rivers, wells, and springs, should not be exploited to the point of depletion.

Two of the strongest arguments for control are the maintenance of power and the national defense. Without the maintenance of adequate power, industries, transportation, domestic and business facilities—in fact, nearly all modern activity—would cease. Far more than in normal times, war requires an exceptional amount of power, without which the fighting forces cannot be properly equipped in their efforts to wage a successful campaign.

Minor methods of control include the rehabilitation of water systems to prevent a wasteful leakage, which can mount to staggering proportions. The metering of all water consumption is another step, since consumers will be more careful of the amount they use if they are charged for the exact amount of water drawn, rather than a flat rate regardless of how much is used. The raising of water rates will also make users more cautious as to the amount of water drawn. More spectacular methods of conservation include flood control and the building of dams and scientifically-sound irrigation canals.

Public power commissions, both state and federal, have been created in an effort to plan such programs effectively. The increasing concern over conservation and control of water power would not be necessary if the sources were unlimited as in the case of wind and air; but, unfortunately, such is not the case.

MAN HARNESSES THE WIND

Air, unlike water, is compressible. For example, a given volume of air, at atmospheric pressure, can be compressed into almost any other given volume. Water, except to a very negligible extent, cannot be so compressed. We are all familiar with the unharnessed power of wind. Common illustrations are cyclones, tornadoes, hurricanes, and ordinary gales. The leashing of this power has long been man's dream, and to some extent it has been realized.

Many stories have been written and told about the picturesque windmills of the Dutch. Windmills are still in common use today, although their setting is probably less romantic. They are primarily used on farms for pumping water. A variation of this use, in recent years, has been the introduction of wind machines which have an electric generator mounted on the propeller shaft of the windmill. When the propeller and its shaft are turned by the wind, electricity is generated which is used to keep storage batteries charged. This system is gaining great popularity in sections

Photo by J. Holken

THE WINDS FURNISH POWER ON THE LOWER RHINE

that are without electrical power lines, particularly in the rural districts.

Another example of the application of wind power is the sailing vessel. For many years this was the chief means of water transportation. Now, however, sailing boats are small sized, as a rule, and are used as pleasure boats.

The greatest power of the air is available when it can be compressed in a container and made to do work upon its expansion or release to normal atmospheric pressure. There are many machines that depend on air power for their operation, and they have proved remarkably successful.

Compressed air may be applied by one of two methods; free action or enclosed action. In the former, the air must escape to do its work; in the latter type, it must be confined to accomplish its purpose. Examples of free action include gas and oil burner air-feeds, sand-blasters, and glass-blowers. Enclosed action is illustrated by those machines that require the expansion of compressed air against a piston to give movement, such as pneumatic hammers, riveters, drills, reamers, and tube expanders. Automobiles, ships, and streetcars are painted by compressed-air paint

Courtesy Ingersoll-Rand

IMPACT WRENCHES BOLTING UP COVER PLATES ON A BRIDGE REPAIR JOB guns, which give a better coat and do the work in a fraction of the time required for hand-painting. Every boy is familiar with the BB gun, or air rifle, with which he shoots tin cans, and which works by being pumped after every shot or series of shots.

The tubes that are used inside of automobile tires hold the car up by means of compressed air. In many stores and offices, communication is possible between different departments through the use of pneumatic tubes of compressed air that carry containers through a network of pipes from one part of a building to another.

THE POWER OF STEAM

Because of the power created by its expansion, steam, like air, has proved to be a major factor in the history of producing usable energy. The discovery of the power in steam brought about an epochal change in industry by effecting an immediate enlargement of factories whose additional power requirements could thus be met. This revolution was especially notable in coal-

Courtesy Allis-Chalmers Co.

80,000 KW. TANDEM COMPOUND STEAM TURBO-ALTERNATOR UNIT

producing areas. Although small mills continued to use water power, the new steam power was responsible for the increased industrial output.

Coal was the first fuel used to fire steam boilers, but the invention of successful oil burners paved the way for a favorable competition with coal.

Steam power is used principally in the generation of electricity. There are, however, many other examples of steam-operated machines, notably, the railroad locomotive. The steam-driven locomotive, however, is being rapidly supplanted by the Diesel-electric train.

There are two main types of steam machinery: the reciprocating engine and the turbine. In the former, steam pressure pushes against a piston connected with a crank that converts the forward and backward movement into rotary motion. In the second, or turbine type, the operation is similar to that of a water turbine. Jets of steam under high pressure hit the projecting vanes on the turbine wheel, causing rotation.

The reciprocating engine develops high power at low speed, while the turbine develops high power at high speed. The reciprocating engine is often used to pump huge quantities of water. The pumping station of large water works may contain an engine whose flywheel is of an enormous size. One such installation has a fire pit that could accommodate fifteen men seated at a table. The turbines are more commonly used in steam-electric generating plants where high speed as well as great power is necessary. Other examples of steam-operated machinery include steam hammers and the very familiar steam shovels.

Steam is not always the cheapest means of power production, since its efficiency is rather low. The reciprocating engine is from ten to thirty per cent efficient. Turbines usually are much more efficient, because they allow a more complete expansion of steam than do reciprocating engines.

INTERNAL COMBUSTION ENGINES

In later years, steam power has encountered a formidable competitor in the internal-combustion engine, which drives our

Courtesy Ford Motor Co.

ASSEMBLING PARTS OF AN INTERNAL COMBUSTION ENGINE
Using efficient modern methods of mass production, automobile engines are built with
speed and precision by these workmen. This scene shows the portion of the plant in which
pistons, connecting rods, wrist pins, and crankshaft bearings, those parts which carry the
power from the cylinder to the crankshaft, are assembled.

automobiles, airplanes, tractors, trucks, and Diesel-electric trains,
to mention only a few of its applications. There are three types
of internal-combustion engines: (a) gas, (b) gasoline, and (c)
Diesel. The gasoline engine is the most popular type for automotive purposes since it must operate efficiently at various speeds
and usually at far below its rated power. The combustion process
requires a spark to ignite the mixture of air and gasoline vapor.

The Diesel type of engine is rapidly establishing a place for
itself as a means of power production. Its most spectacular application at the present time is as a prime mover for Diesel-electric
streamlined trains. Since this type of engine operates most efficiently at a constant speed, it is used on trains to drive electric
generators that supply current to the electric motors on the trucks
of the power cars. Unlike the gasoline engine, the Diesel type does
not require a spark plug for ignition; the heat resulting from com-

pression suffices to ignite the mixture. This engine is fueled with light crude oil, which, at present, is more economical than gasoline.

A third type of internal-combustion engine is one which uses for its fuel different grades of natural or manufactured gas. Sewage-disposal plants make use of gas engines for their motive power to some extent, because gas is a by-product of their purification process.

The efficiency of internal-combustion engines is fairly high, ranging from forty per cent upward. This, of course, refers only to the thermal or heat efficiency, the ratio of heat units put into the engine in the form of fuel, and the heat units turned out by the engine in the form of horsepower. Another factor must be taken into consideration in the selection of a motive power unit, namely the economic efficiency or the total cost of running it. Situations exist where an engine of high thermal efficiency is too expensive to operate; in such cases it is cheaper to install a mechanically less efficient one and still obtain a higher economic efficiency.

THE ENERGY THAT ILLUMINATES THE WORLD

Electricity revolutionized industry when it succeeded steam in much the same manner as industry was affected when steam superseded water as a source of power. Steam power was not, however, to pass out of the picture, but merely to assume a new role. Prior to the advent of electricity, each factory or plant was required to maintain its own steam plant, buy its own coal, and engage in a hundred other cumbersome activities. Formerly, power in the form of fuel had to be brought to each individual plant; with the utilization of electricity it became possible to bring the fuel to one central plant, where it could turn electrical generators and send electricity over wires to wherever it was needed. Thus were many manufacturers and other users of steam power able to abandon their own costly individual power plants and receive their power requirements over wires from a central generating station.

The tremendous energy that electricity is capable of producing is vividly illustrated by a very common occurrence—lightning.

Its far-reaching and unharnessed power has been responsible for such destruction as the splitting of huge redwood trees, the explosion of gasoline, oil, and gas storage-tanks, and costly fires. Engineering science, through careful and painstaking research over a period of many years, has made available controlled electricity that is almost equally as powerful.

Electricity is generated in either direct current (D.C.) or alternating current (A.C.). Direct current, as its name implies, is that type in which the electricity flows in one direction only, from the generator through a wire into and through a connected appliance, and then back along a second wire to the generator, thereby completing a circuit. Alternating current, while it uses the same wire circuit, has an oscillating motion by which it travels first in one direction and then reverses itself to travel in the opposite direction. One complete oscillation is called a "cycle." This type is used mainly in residential sections and for transmission over long distances. Sixty-cycle alternating current, the type ordinarily used in homes, makes sixty complete oscillations in one second.

The number of cycles of an alternating current per second is called the "frequency," which is a common term to radio owners. The frequency of a radio station is expressed in kilocycles (thousands of cycles) and the radio dial is set at the number of kilocycles corresponding to a particular broadcasting station. The incredible number of possible direction-changes per second of an alternating current may be illustrated by a radio station whose frequency is 1550 kilocycles, or 1,550,000 cycles, per second. Short-wave broadcasting utilizes frequencies of even higher value.

Both direct current and alternating current have their respective advantages and disadvantages. Direct current cannot be generated in excess of 600 volts, which means that it cannot be transmitted over long distances. Even if higher D.C. voltages could be generated, the size of the wire required to transmit it would prohibit its use. However, electricity used for commercial purposes, such as in printing-presses, streetcars, and elevators, is often direct, as they operate much better with this type of current. Its use is

Courtesy Textile Machine Works

A BATTERY OF TRANSFORMERS

confined more or less to large cities or industrial sections, where
transmission distances are not great.

Alternating current, on the other hand, can be generated at
high voltages. Installations of generators have been made that
are capable of turning out 13,800 volts. Generation capacities
are usually expressed in kilowatts, or thousands of watts. (A watt
is the product of the voltage times the current.) Some stations
in this country have generators capable of producing 100,000
kilowatts. Huge transformers are used when the current is to be
sent great distances. The step-up transformer employed increases
the voltage at the expense of diminishing the current.

When the alternating current arrives at its destination, probably as far as 300 or 400 miles from the generating station, it en-
counters other transformers that reverse the procedure; they are
step-downs, which lower the voltage and increase the current to
usable quantities. The purpose of the first transformer is to provide enough voltage, or pressure, to send the current great distances. Ordinary wire can handle this electricity because the
current has been stepped down, and the size of the wire required
depends partly upon the amount of current being carried.

Homer Smith photo, Chicago
WATER POWER DEVELOPMENT AT IMATIA, FINLAND

WATERFALLS AND POWER

The first type of power employed by generating stations to turn their generators was water power. A tremendous volume of water surged through huge turbines, which in turn rotated the generators. In later years, however, circumstances sometimes made it desirable to erect plants where sufficient water power did not exist. The steam turbine then was used as a prime mover, and pioneering engineers performed remarkable work on the development and improvement of the steam turbine, so that today some steam plants can challenge the newer hydroelectric stations in capacity as well as in efficiency. Recently the tide of popularity has again swung to water power with the achievement of some of the most spectacular engineering feats known to man, namely the construction of such large dams as the Norris, Boulder, and Bonneville.

The Diesel internal-combustion engine has proved a success as a prime mover for the generators in some of our smaller cities that have not as yet availed themselves of the vast network of electrical power systems covering the country.

USES OF ELECTRIC POWER

The users of electricity find a host of tasks for this great unseen force to perform. It has been made to lift bridges; to run streetcars; to operate everything from an electric shaver to a 5,400-horsepower, transcontinental railroad train; and even to smash the lowly atom. Industry is the greatest user of electric motors for power purposes; the motors range anywhere from the size needed to operate a sewing machine to gigantic dynamos that furnish power for the machinery of an entire factory.

Illumination is probably the next most common use of electricity. No motors are in operation here; the electric current enters a light bulb and heats a filament until it glows. Alternating current is almost universally used for lighting, except in direct-current districts and on streetcars where the lights obtain their power from the same source as do the motors, and in a few other exceptional instances.

Electric heating is a field that has in recent years been holding the attention of engineers and laymen alike. Common illustrations are the ordinary home bathroom heaters, streetcar heaters, and the electric cooking range. Research is being conducted on the heating of entire homes by electrical means. Electric irons for pressing also utilize the heating properties of electricity.

THE ELECTRIC BATTERY

Another main source of electric energy is the electric battery, which generates electricity by chemical reactions between suitable substances. The storage battery, the most common type, has a number of uses. The ignition, starter, generator, and electrical accessories, such as radio, heater, lights, and fan, indicate the important part it plays in the electrical equipment of an automobile.

Storage batteries have many other commercial uses, particularly as "stand-by," or emergency, equipment. Generating stations, radio-broadcasting stations, telephone companies, and even some hospitals are equipped with enough batteries to take over their load requirements in the event of a power failure on their regular lines. These batteries are assembled in such quantity and

42C10

A 42-CELL STOR-
AGE BATTERY

Courtesy Thomas A.
Edison, Inc.

arrangement that they may replace the whole load of their circuit for a period ranging from a few hours to a number of days.

Another type of battery called the "dry cell" is not in quite as wide use as the storage battery, although in the early days of radio it was a most necessary adjunct. The main purpose of the dry cell is to serve as an intermittent supply of electricity for such appliances as doorbells, buzzers, telephone bells, and flashlights. The name "dry cell" is actually a misnomer, since no electricity would flow if it were actually dry, but it is so called because the liquid contents are not visible as in the wet storage battery, nor does it require replenishing. The chief reason for the failure of a dry cell to deliver current is that it has actually become dry. All electricity from the dry cell as well as from the wet storage battery is of the direct-current type.

THE APPLICATION OF POWER

The main objective of an engineer in dealing with the application of power, is to get work done as quickly and as efficiently as possible without sacrificing its quality. In some types of industry speed is of prime importance, and the problem becomes one of obtaining a maximum of speed from an allotted amount of power.

Speed is essential in the generation of electricity, since the generated voltage is directly dependent upon the swiftness of the spin of the generator's armature. Hence, when steam power is used for turning the generators, turbines are employed instead of reciprocating engines, because of their greater speed properties. Both of these engines produce power, but speed demands the turbine.

The machining of tool and implement parts is an example of the industrial demand for a wide range of power and speed. Some metals must be machined rapidly to prevent the cutting tool from gouging the material. This is most important when we realize that parts for an automobile engine, for example, must be machined to limits as fine as one ten-thousandth part of an inch. Greater speed produces a greater number of pieces per man or machine in a definite working period, reduces an article's cost and places it in the hands of a larger number of people.

The speed of moving vehicles is especially important in aviation. Airplanes would fall if they did not move swiftly. Their very speed holds them up, compressing the air underneath the wings and forming a partial vacuum above. Speed is a prime factor in the modern world. Railroads and airplanes, automobiles and ships—all seek to move faster and faster, as if they were in a world-wide race. The purpose of the engineer at all times is to utilize power in such a manner as will provide the necessary speed, do the work efficiently, and pay the power-user a reasonable profit.

There is a very definite relation between speed and power. The expression "an 85-horsepower motor" designates the ultimate power the motor is capable of producing at its maximum or near-maximum speed. Some machines that are required to deliver power at their maximum speed are run constantly at that speed; if their speed were constantly varying, their efficiency would be very low and they would prove costly to operate; too much power would be expended in changing the speed of the motor itself, in overcoming the inertia of its heavy parts. However, most motors are not very efficient when running at their maximum speed. Experimentation will discover for each motor the speed at which its output will most nearly equal its intake of power, or its fuel consumption. That speed is its most efficient one, although it may

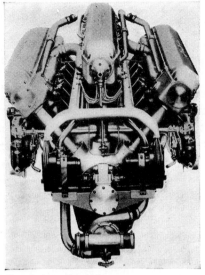

Courtesy Isotta-Fraschini

ITALIAN V-12 AUTOMOBILE
ENGINE

often have to be run faster to keep the wheels of industry turning at the rate the modern world demands.

The gasoline type of internal-combustion engine is comparatively efficient at all speeds. Of course, it delivers its maximum horsepower at a point near its maximum speed, but fuel consumption is greater at higher speeds. This engine has proved quite satisfactory on the basis of power output in relation to any speed. The flexibility of operation of modern motor cars would not be possible if this were not true. Present-day driving conditions call for the entire speed range of the automobile engine. Automotive engineers have labored long and unceasingly to bring this type of power generator to its present degree of efficiency. They have made this engine more powerful and more flexible, with an almost instantaneous response and a more economic consumption of fuel. It is a far cry from the two-cylinder, ten-horsepower "rip snorter" of thirty-five years ago that propelled a vehicle at the breath-taking speed of almost fifteen miles an hour to the modern, twelve-cylinder racing car capable of roaring along at 200 miles an hour because of the 725-horsepower engine under its hood.

The relation of power to speed varies when considering steam machinery. The reciprocating steam engine is capable of delivering high quantities of power at low speeds, the ordinary steam engine not exceeding, as a rule, 200 revolutions a minute. The turbine, as stated before, delivers high power at high speeds. The steam is fed to the turbine blades from nozzles under high pressure, and the turbine allows for a more complete expansion of the steam than does the reciprocating engine, a factor which accounts for the former's comparatively high efficiency. Terrific speeds are possible with the steam turbine. In one instance, the Don turbine attained a velocity of 35,000 revolutions per minute in torpedo work, and operated regularly at 25,000.

The speed of running water used as a source of power does not affect the power derived unless one compares an equal volume of water in the two cases. We can readily see that a tremendous flow, at a nine-inch height, falling comparatively slowly over the nine inches might produce greater power than a smaller volume falling much faster from a greater height. Of course, if equal volumes are assumed in both cases then speed and head will naturally make a difference in power.

THE TRANSMISSION OF POWER

The next consideration in the utilization of power is its transmission, accomplished in many ways. The most obvious and familiar method is by means of mechanical devices. Methods are simple and complex, but in general the transmitting of power is done by means of belts, chains, ropes, gears, shafts, and clutches. The engineer is constantly striving to make these devices as efficient as possible. However, some of the power that is transmitted must necessarily be used to overcome the friction and the weight of these parts.

Transmission may be accomplished by any of the previously mentioned transmitting devices, alone or in combination. Factories generally employ a single prime mover and transmit its power to various machines requiring it for their operation. For example, a belt on the main wheel of the prime mover transmits its power to a line shaft. Smaller wheels, placed advantageously along this shaft, transmit power through other belts that go to small countershafts carrying fixed and loose pulleys and striking gears that allow any particular machine to be started or stopped at will, even while the main shafts are rotating. The power is then sent by chains or belts from these fixed and loose pulleys to the individual machine itself.

Gears are perhaps the oldest known power-transmitting devices. They are used extensively in machinery of all types, but most of us are familiar with them only in the automobile. If two cylinders on parallel shafts are placed so their rims touch, one may drive the other by friction. If slotted teeth are cut into the rims of each, the teeth become enmeshed, with the result that one cylinder will drive the other by exerting a force on the face of the teeth of the gear to be moved.

Belts are perhaps the next most familiar means of transmitting power. A visit to a fair-sized machine shop will reveal to the uninitiated an astounding array of belts leading from shaft to shaft, and then to individual machines.

Driving machines by chains is also a popular method, an outstanding illustration of which is the sprocket chain of a bicycle. Flat-linked chains are constructed in an endless form and the slots engage the gear teeth of the wheel. As a particular link approaches the rim of the gear, a tooth on the gear will fall into the link and drive the chain or be driven by the chain. Another use of the chain drive is seen in the old-style motor truck that was propelled by a chain from a shaft to each of the rear wheels.

Rope drives are like chain drives, except that when rope is used it is generally wound around a drum on the prime mover and, by encircling a grooved wheel-rim, moves it by friction.

Courtesy Chain Belt Co., Milwaukee

THE CHAIN DRIVE IS EFFICIENT AND POSITIVE IN ACTION

Ropes are commonly used in lifting either directly by one pulley, or by an assembly of pulleys. On heavy work particularly, the driving wheel may have its rim cut into a number of grooves to accommodate more than one rope. The steel cable, a variation of the rope drive, is capable of doing work greatly beyond the endurance of ordinary rope. Cranes, steam shovels, and other equipment of flexible operation frequently use wire cable, or wire rope as it is sometimes called.

Homer Smith photo, Chicago

A MODERN MACHINE SHOP IN BUENOS AIRES, ARGENTINA

Courtesy Link-Belt Company

A DIESEL-POWERED LOCOMOTIVE CRANE WITH LIFT-
ING MAGNET FOR USE IN HANDLING SCRAP IRON
A complex system of pulleys transfers power from the engine.

Courtesy Allis-Chalmers Company

TURNING AN IMMENSE TWO-THROW CRANKSHAFT

The clutch, perhaps most commonly used in automobiles, is a power-transmission device that operates through the force of friction, but in a manner somewhat different from that of the rope drive. Its principle of operation may be demonstrated by using two sheets of sandpaper. If one is placed with its rough surface upward and the other laid against it with its rough surface downward, rotation of the top sheet causes the bottom sheet to rotate also. An automobile clutch acts in the same way, but it is assembled to operate in an upright position. One face of the clutch is mounted on the crankshaft, which comes from the engine; the other, on the drive shaft, which is connected with the transmission, or shifting gears, of the automobile. The two faces, or sets of faces, are brought together by releasing the clutch-pedal, or are thrown apart by pushing it down.

ELIMINATING VIBRATION AND FRICTION

Machines that move, and many that do not move, have what is called a vibration point. Auto drivers are familiar with the fact that at certain engine speeds the whole body of the car seems to vibrate. This is due to the synchronization of the vibration point of the engine to the vibration point of the car body. Sometimes these vibrating forces assume tremendous proportions and do extreme damage. It is not difficult to imagine what would happen to a steam turbine rotating at 8,000 revolutions per minute if all whirling parts were not balanced perfectly. The centrifugal force would tear the machinery to pieces. Automotive engineers have done much to eliminate vibration by devising counterbalanced crankshafts of better construction, rubber engine-mountings, rubber body-mountings, and friction-free coil springs for wheel suspension.

The force of vibration takes a great deal of useful power away from the ultimate objective and thereby lowers the efficiency of a power-transmission system. Extensive research in the past has done much to eliminate harmful vibration from machinery, but there is a continuous effort to perfect present power-producing and transmitting machinery. This research into better methods is largely a matter of engineering, with invaluable assistance, of course, from the world of pure science. In setting out to find a better method or a better machine the engineer knows what he wants and so progresses logically and analytically to his goal. Sometimes he attains it, and sometimes he does not. If he fails, he merely starts out again along another line of reasoning.

Research into power machinery and power transmission has concerned itself more and more with the problem of friction. An absolutely frictionless moving part is impossible, even if it could turn freely and unsuspended in air, but the aim is to approach the perfect state as closely as possible. There are two major methods of attacking this problem: first, the improvement of bearings; and second, an attempt to make the machines simpler in design, that is, with fewer moving parts.

Men constantly experiment upon materials to see if stronger metal can be produced to give longer wear, a more nearly frictionless bearing-surface, and greater endurance under extreme operating conditions. The question of lubrication is also an important one; engineers in this field constantly seek to make oils and greases give more efficient service. There is a continuous study to find new fuels for prime movers, while efforts are ever being made to get as much power out of a unit quantity of fuel as possible.

Observation of the types of power machines best suited to certain conditions is also an unceasing activity. It is obvious that a slow-speed, though high-powered, steam engine would not be suitable to turn a high-speed electric generator if complicated gearing were necessary to attain the desired speed, since the high-speed turbine with no intermediate gearing can produce the same results in a more suitable manner.

THE ENGINEER AS INVENTOR

When no existing machine can be altered to give better service, the engineer attempts to create a new one, perhaps entirely revolutionary in design and operation. This is the process we call invention. The devising of new industrial methods, as opposed to the invention of new machines, is also an engineering procedure. The engineer or scientist has a fundamental knowledge of the laws of nature, physics, and other sciences, and often he is able to arrive at a solution resulting in an entirely new invention. Long hard work is one of the prime requisites, but when he sees his labors crowned with success, he considers himself well rewarded.

The modern electric light, to take a familiar example, is not the result of mere chance, but the fruition of years of long laboring on the part of one of our best-known inventors and scientists, Thomas A. Edison. On the other hand, we also have inventions, any number of them, that are the result of chance discoveries. Often we see the inventor and his works ridiculed by the public in general. An outstanding example of this is the automobile. Many an early owner of the roaring, fire-spitting, smoke-belching contraption was jeered at, and told to get a "hay-burner" instead of his "gasoline-burner." Today, however, we realize what an important role the automobile has assumed in our everyday lives.

While we may think that nearly everything that could be invented has been invented, man continues his striving to perfect the machines of industry and the conveniences of life in general.

Courtesy Kansas City, Mo., Chamber of Commerce

MUNICIPAL AUDITORIUM, KANSAS CITY, MISSOURI

New methods of doing things are constantly being devised, and, if they prove worthy, they are accepted; if they are unworthy, they are either discarded or improved upon to make them useful. The same holds true of the machines that lighten our tasks and make life more enjoyable. The work is not easy, but its results are certainly worth the effort.

The aim behind most of the work that deals with the efficiency of machines and methods is to produce better machinery, better working conditions, and better products. Efforts are constantly being made to eliminate wasteful operations and processes which are costly and add to the expense of manufacturing an article. Time-study engineers devote their entire efforts toward making work progress smoothly, efficiently, and without an unnecessary duplication of processes. The scientific study of power machinery is one step toward lower production costs. The power must be produced or obtained as cheaply as possible, and it must be used as efficiently as conditions will permit. Unceasing efforts are being made to use as high a percentage of the acquired power as possible. The study of efficient power-transmission equipment is given just as much consideration as power-producing equipment.

Safer and more healthful working conditions are very desirable in an industrial plant, because they allow the workman to put forth his best and most productive efforts; they prolong the period of his productive ability; and they raise his morale, which will, in turn, make him a better citizen. In short, if the employer takes pains to provide for his worker's welfare, the employee will prove to be a more loyal workman and a credit to his community. The products that finally emerge from an efficiently run plant will be lower in cost, better in quality, and greater in quantity.

Much remains to be done, but already the engineer has contributed invaluable services in promoting the wealth, luxury, and security of the modern world. His striving for perfection has certainly not been in vain. When we see everywhere around us the results of his conversion of nature's tremendous energy and power into useful products, only then do we realize the miracles that have been accomplished.

Courtesy The Art Institute of Chicago

OLDEST SOURCE OF POWER
Watermills, such as this one in Wales, furnished man with power
long before the advent of other forms.

ENGINEERING HAS created a new pattern in the development of modern industrial processes. It has made a systematic science out of an occult art. The day of the romanticized inventor, puttering about in his cellar workshop with a jumble of bottles, springs, and rubber bands, is gone. Spectacular discoveries and heroic advances continue and increase, but much of the hit or miss manner in which they were formerly made has disappeared.

The achievements of the old-time inventors were occasional spurts of luck which punctuated long years of futile dabbling and systemless, uncoördinated experiment. The achievements of anonymous modern engineers flow, instead, in a constant stream from great laboratories in which unproductive effort has been largely eliminated. There is little hullabaloo over the majority of discoveries of modern engineers; most of them are never heard of except among a small group of scientists. But their application to the activities of everyday life benefits the entire world.

NONE THE LESS DREAMS

Yet the engineer is no machine. His dreams, though intelligently systematic, are none the less dreams. But, the very fact that an attack on a particular problem is systematically organized often leads to unsuspected discoveries which spring suddenly from an obscure part of a routine task. Engineers were trying only to improve the quality of crude oil when the "oil cracking" process of producing gasoline was discovered.

Years before the first, rattling Model T Fords bounced along dirt roads, engineers set out to solve a problem. The slimy crude oil, which was pumped from the ground or which gushed forth violently from towering derricks, contained obstinate particles of water, which, engineers were informed, must be removed. Gasoline and kerosene were already being obtained by heating the crude oil until the boiling point of one and then another of these products was reached. At these points the substances rose in vapor and were distilled. The water particles suspended in the oil hampered the whole process, and the experimenters decided to try heating the crude oil to a temperature far above the boiling point of any of the component liquids. They wanted to see if the bothersome water particles could be forced out by the combination of high temperature and intense pressure.

What they discovered, to their amazement, was that the pressure and temperature broke down the molecules of crude oil into the lighter molecules of gasoline. Here, in the distillate of this "cracking" process, they were startled to find that they had a new way to make gasoline. The whole world of gasoline-powered industry, from mighty gasoline-driven generators to gasoline-electric trains, benefited, as did the drivers of automobiles, by a cheaper, effective gasoline.

Everywhere engineers make easier the turning of the wheels within wheels that constitute our inter-related system of industries. Major among these turning wheels are the groups of industries which create consumers' and producers' goods. Geared into the former group are the great individual industries, such as the manufacturing of automobiles or telephones; and into the latter, such industries as aluminum and steel. Within these industries are the vital activities of sales and production, which are meshed with the wheels of management: power, machinery, and personnel. And the system is even more complicated. Power, which is one small cog in the manufacture of radio apparatus, is in itself a mighty enterprise, and steel, also one of the mighty industries, furnishes the raw material for a thousand other industries.

Everywhere in the great machine of modern industry is the engineer, improving chemical processes and increasing the efficiency of management, inventing manufacturing techniques, and sweating over production and distribution graphs. He is the man with the charts, the test tubes, and the stop watches. Estimating, experimenting, and eliminating waste and error, he lets no part of the industrial machine escape his penetrating eye.

APPARATUS FOR
DE-GASSING
METALS

Courtesy General
Electric Company

BLUEPRINTS, TEST TUBES, AND STOP WATCHES

The engineer examines each step of each industrial process, like a boy taking apart his father's watch to see what makes it tick. The difference is that the engineer finds out what makes the industrial process tick and in addition continually devises methods of making it tick better. Before each process begins, the engineer has done his research, made his drawings, and tested his models. When Diesel-electric power was perfected, the problems of adapting it to fast trains were left to the engineers to solve. Rushing over the rails at high speeds, the train had to be constructed so that it would not fly apart when the metals were subjected to tremendous strains. At the same time the engineers were told that they were working on a high-speed train which must not be burdened with heavy metal or massive construction. Make it strong but make it light—that was the order.

Into the metallurgical laboratories went the engineers, blending metals, pouring molten alloy after alloy, testing the resistance of the mixed metals to strain and to heat, testing their flexibility. Some were too brittle; some were very strong but so pliable that they would have bent out of shape every time the train rounded a curve. The metals which were strong and flexible in the correct proportions were then weighed to see if they were light enough. If the results were not satisfactory the engineers started over again using different alloys, making new tests. During patient weeks of experiment, they tested, made calculations and experiments, and tested again. Steel alloyed with shining chromium proved to possess great tensile strength and to be light enough for the streamliners. Further tests for strain proved that welding the metal for the train would make for stronger car bodies than the old technique of riveting could.

RAINDROP STREAMLINING

Into the hands of the engineers dropped another problem. If streamlining was the type of design which would allow trains to run at higher speeds than they could if they were covered with bulky projecting networks of pipes, rods, and tubing, what was the best kind of streamlining? A raindrop, being liquid, is molded by the air it passes through so that it meets with the least possible resistance. But did the same problems exist for a train moving along the ground instead of freely through the air? Back to their laboratories went the engineers. They built models and wind tunnels in which resistance to air could be measured. They tried out all sorts of shapes in their trains and discovered that the raindrop design was unworkable. In the first place, of course, they had to consider problems of freight and passenger transportation, of existing rails and tunnels and bridges. But even a reasonable adaptation of the raindrop design was unworkable. The bulb-front trains "nosed" about, with a tendency to leave the rails and soar into the air. They discovered that a certain amount of air pressure, acting downward on a plow-like front, was necessary to prevent this "nosing" action.

DETACHABLE SLEEVES

Other problems arose when the streamliners were put into actual use. The six hundred horse-power Diesel engines, driving the trains along at speeds well over a hundred miles an hour, wore

Courtesy General Electric Company

In the great electric locomotives which are coming into increased use, the engineer has a comfortable seat in a smoke- and soot-free cab. The operating devices are little different from those of the ordinary electric streetcar.

out their cylinders. The speed and friction were too great for any known type of construction material. So the engineers again turned anonymous inventors and devised a "sleeve" which could be fitted into the cylinder. When the powerful Diesel wore the metal of the sleeve down so that engine compression began to be lost, the sleeve was simply taken out and a new one inserted. Without this device a streamliner would need a new engine block so often that its operation would be impractical. The nameless brotherhood of engineers systematically pooled their mental resources and research facts and conquered the obstacle simply and scientifically.

THE ENGINEER WITH A TEST TUBE

Continually mixing and testing, translating mathematical formulas into white hot metals and bubbling chemical compounds, and from the metals and chemicals discovering new formulas, the chemical engineers give the world new alloys, new materials and substances. For the photographer and the motion picture studio they concoct endless varieties of sensitive photo films; for the dressmaker they invent new kinds of cloth. The housewife pours her mushroom soup from scientifically prepared "tin" cans, in which the engineer uses little tin; her clothes are rescued from the ravages of moths by chemical sentries provided by the engineer; and chemical engineering gives her the assortment of soaps which protect her complexion, scour her floors, and gently cleanse her linens.

It is the engineer who devises methods of making lead pencils without lead, wooden objects without wood, rice paper without rice, and chamois skin without chamois leather. He fights cold when it freezes automobile radiators and shrinks vinegar and rails and wires. He concocts insulation and anti-freeze and new techniques of chemical and electrical heating. He combats dampness which mildews cloth, rusts metal, and snaps violin strings. He mixes paint and builds batteries. He tests concrete and rubber, bakelite and glass, experimenting and calculating in solving the problems of the modern industrial world.

WHERE CHEMICAL ENGINEERS WORK THEIR MAGIC

No hit-or-miss methods here! The modern industrial laboratory weighs and measures and tests every conceivable material and ingredient to almost infinitesimal exactitude.

SPEAKING A LANGUAGE ALL THEIR OWN

Chemists and chemical engineers could make little headway against the problems of compounds and mixtures as long as they used the cumbersome and primitive language of everyday life. Just as a science of thermodynamics could not progress far when limited to the use of such terms as "lukewarm" and "fairly chilly," chemistry was handicapped in trying to construct a science with mere words—salt and fire, dirt and air, and bitter and sticky. When the names of the products of chemical engineering are written out in words, they are bulky and confusing. For example, the technical name of aspirin is the mono-acetic acid ester of salicylic acid, but in the language of the chemical engineer the substance, in its empirical formula, is simply $C_9H_8O_4$. This efficient language goes even further in the simplification of understanding complex chemicals by creating map-words of these symbols, which tell the engineer at a glance more of the composition and structure of his subject than can be told in a five-minute discussion.

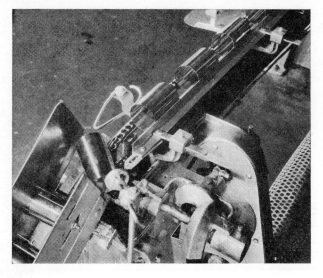

ON THE LINE IN
A TIN CAN
FACTORY
The cans have had
their sides soldered on
the outside instead of
the inside.

SETTING NATURE'S CLOCK AHEAD

Sometimes Mother Nature is a good chemical engineer, but sometimes impatient men find her processes woefully slow. Men wanted a substance which could be molded when it was soft but which could be hardened when it had been made into the desired shape. Mother Nature could make it, but she took a long time about it. She could take the gum from cone-bearing trees and soak it in sea water until it was the hard golden substance called amber; but it took her centuries to do it. Clay was malleable enough, but its hardening in shape was not permanent. It was brittle and tended to dry into dust, but worst of all it would erode if immersed in water.

Engineers worked out various solutions by using hard rubber, but here too were difficulties. Eventually they produced a substance whose use is so familiar that it is difficult to imagine a world without it. That substance is bakelite, which, although it has been in existence for less than three decades since it was invented in 1909, is used in myriad products and processes of modern industry. Bakelite and the many similar materials which have been

developed since its creation are
found in telephones and double
sockets, in trays and handles, in
fountain pens and in a vast
number of industrial machines
and gadgets.

WHY NOT ACCEPT A SUBSTITUTE?

Another of Mother Nature's
aspects which has been given a
good deal of attention by the
chemical engineers is her indif-

Courtesy Bakelite Corporation

A RADIO CABINET OF MOULDED
BAKELITE

ference to costs and prices. Needless to say, these are of considerable interest to men, and the engineers strive constantly to dupli-
cate natural materials at less expense than is needed to take them directly from nature. Mother Nature unfortunately planted rubber
trees at a rather great distance from Akron, buried her glittering
diamonds far from the factories where diamond points are a neces-

Courtesy Bakelite Corporation

AN EARLY BAKELITE STILL
Dr. Baekeland's first semi-commercial unit
used in his Yonkers laboratory.

sary adjunct to fine cutting, and
grew the mulberry trees, on
which silkworms feed, a long
way from the textile centers of
the modern industrial world.

So, into the hands of the
engineers were thrust the problems of creating substitutes for
rubber and diamonds and silk
and a thousand other materials
in whose production nature was
not sufficiently generous.

Engineering is still working
on many of these problems.
Artificial rubber can be made
but still not as well as the trees
make it. In compounds of tungsten, that amazing metal which

is used in the filaments of electric light bulbs and in phonograph needles, the chemical engineers discovered a partial substitute for costly diamonds. Cutting tools made of tungsten carbide are nearly as efficient as diamonds even when the friction of cutting has made them red hot. In competing with the silkworm, engineering has been very successful. Celanese, rayon, and other cellulose fabrics have been so perfected that their better grades are in many ways actually far superior to silk. Other materials, substitutes for natural substances, have been produced in great numbers by the prolific chemical engineers. They have perfected stainless steel, pyrex glass which will not fracture even when exposed to great heat, and artificial leathers, woods, and stones. Of course Mother Nature supplies the raw materials out of which the engineers create new substances. She gives them her elements, the molecules of the elements, and the atoms of the molecules, but it is their task to fit these tiny particles together, like the parts of a jigsaw puzzle, building new forms of matter and energy. The variety of possible substances is almost infinite. The organic compounds alone, the materials in which carbon is combined with such other elements as hydrogen and oxygen, are so many and so diverse that their surface has scarcely been scratched. What will be produced when the chemical engineers begin to plumb the depths so far unfathomed is the stuff of which engineering dreams are made.

There is a substance, one of an endless series of chemicals, which is a compound of chlorine and fluorine. It is called dichlorodifluoromethane, and for many years it was just another chemical. It had been synthesized, just to prove that it could be made, but it was just another laboratory toy until the chemical engineer discovered that it was a far better refrigerant than any of the other substances that had been used before. It was not only an efficient refrigerating substance; it was safer for the many uses to which refrigerants are put. It was non-inflammable. Flowing in gaseous form across a burning flame it did not ignite; in fact it was the flame which was in danger of being extinguished by the gas. The refrigerating agent was non-poisonous—breathed into the lungs of man there was no deadly effect like that produced by some earlier substances.

AN ASSISTANT THE ENGINEER CANNOT SEE

Sometimes the engineer accomplishes his miracles with the coal and iron and manganese brought up from mines far beneath the surface of the earth. Sometimes he mixes the produce of soy bean plants or green fields of yellow-tipped corn or the snow-dotted fields of cotton. At other times he calls in assistants, living beings known as bacteria. The men who do this work aided by bacteria are called biochemical engineers. Exploring the "misty mid-region" between the physical and the biological sciences, this branch of engineering contributes not only to efficiency in industrial production but to health and sanitation as well.

Biochemical science lends its assistance in another problem confronting the engineer—namely, the treatment of sewage to render it harmless. When we are told the sewage which is treated each day by the city of Chicago alone equals the normal flow of the Thames River above London, we realize the size of the work and the importance of the operations.

Courtesy Link-Belt Company

SLUDGE SETTLING TANKS, CITY OF SPRINGFIELD, ILLINOIS

In modern sewage treatment plants, a gas similar to natural gas is given off. This is largely the hydrocarbon known as methane or marsh gas. It is collected and stored in tanks, generally in sufficient quantities to operate all the pumps and machinery of the plant. At the beginning of the operations all combustible materials are screened out. Enough gas is also available in sufficient quantities to incinerate this material, burning it at so high a temperature that all gases are completely oxidized and nothing is left to cause an objectionable odor. Even with all these uses there is still enough gas left over to regulate the temperature in other parts of the plant.

Most systems of sewage disposal are basically quite similar. The first step is to screen out all organic matter and incinerate it. Next sand, grit, cinders, and other inorganic matter are removed by allowing them to settle while the velocity of the incoming stream of sewage is checked. When dried this material is porous. The free circulation of air which contains oxygen either kills harmful germs by direct oxidation, or causes other germs, which consume the harmful ones, to multiply.

The remaining sewage is a liquid with fine bits of evil-smelling garbage in it. This material is run into large tanks where there is no appreciable velocity. Here, the minute particles of organic matter settle to the bottom and are drawn off, leaving behind a clear, relatively harmless liquid at the surface of the tanks. As the organic matter settles, it carries most of the harmful bacteria with it. It is their food supply; they cling to it and are carried to the bottom and drawn off into digesting tanks.

In these tanks, the temperature is kept at the most suitable degree for the development of anaerobic bacteria. These bacteria, which cannot live in the open air, are introduced to the sewage by pumping back some of the previous batch of digested matter which has already been consumed by the garbage-eating bacteria. In the dark chambers they multiply rapidly, destroying their more harmful brother germs and changing the organic matter into a product like leaf mold and black earth. In this operation, they give off great quantities of gas, sufficient to supply all of the plant mechanisms and still leave a surplus to sell or burn.

The digested material is called sludge. At intervals it is drained from the digestion tanks upon beds of coarse sand. It contains no harmful bacteria, and the anaerobic bacteria, man's helpers who have cheerfully eaten their fellows, are soon killed by exposure to fresh air and light. When the sludge dries, it makes an excellent nitrogenous fertilizer.

The clear liquid, which came off the top when the sludge was removed, is treated by aerobic bacteria, which thrive in fresh air and sunshine. Sometimes, such conditions are imitated artificially by pumping warm air through the liquid. In other cases, the liquid is sprayed over a deep porous bed of crushed rock. As it slowly trickles down through the rocks it is given a maximum contact with fresh air. What harmful bacteria are not killed by oxidation are consumed by the aerobic bacteria. The final liquid is practically harmless, almost free of organic matter.

Any remaining small amounts of organic matter or harmful micro-organisms can be oxidized instantly by the application of a little liquefied gas. When the biochemical engineer—the sanitary engineer—lets the resulting product run away to the nearest river, he has rendered the once dangerous sewage entirely harmless.

Courtesy Link-Belt Company

ACTIVATED SLUDGE PLANT AT NEW CANAAN, CONNECTICUT

Thanks to the sanitary engineer and his little "bugs," if bacteria may be so called, scourges like typhoid fever have all but vanished from the earth. Where once whole cities were ravaged by this dread disease, most families living today, only thirty years later and in the same cities, have never known an actual case of typhoid fever.

THE MAN WITH THE RUBBER GLOVES

Side by side with the engineers who mix steel with chromium, zinc with antimony, cellulose with nitrates, and nitric acid with toluene are their engineering brothers who provide the power which turns these substances into useful metals, leather, and explosives. In these fields the electrical engineer is part of a greater industry, but in such enterprises as radio, telegraph, and telephone communication he is the mainspring of the industrial structure. Everywhere the wheels of industry are turned by the great force with which Franklin dabbled and which Faraday started on its path to pre-eminence in power production. And everywhere electricity is used the engineer stands by, guiding its production in great generators and its application to the motors which drive mighty liners across roaring oceans and which push traveling cranes carrying tons of molten iron in great crucibles through the steel mills. In the thousand uses of electricity, in electric furnaces, lighting plants, radio transmitters, and motors it is the engineer who keeps production at maximum efficiency.

NIAGARA AND THE MAN-MADE NIAGARAS

The great water generators, such as those at Niagara Falls, the imposing dam system of the Tennessee Valley, Boulder Dam on the Colorado River, and the great Dneprostroi plant in Russia have captured the imagination of the world. One of the greatest of all engineers, Nikola Tesla, designed the Niagara plant as well as the alternating current induction motor which uses its power, and he may well stand as the symbol of the unsung men who quietly go about the huge tasks which power generation involves.

Courtesy Canadian National Railways

A STRIKING VIEW OF NIAGARA FALLS

Crude ancestors of the mighty waterfall power-producers were the water wheels of ancient Egypt. The direct application of the power of water was slow and inefficient, but the perfection of the electric generator multiplied this energy many fold. But men were not content to utilize only the water falls of nature; heroically they set about building new ones of their own. These man-made cataracts did more than supply power to electric generators; they controlled floods, made navigation possible, aided irrigation and forestry, produced chemicals for fertilizers and explosives, as well as served as a source of cheap electricity for the entire surrounding region.

RECLAIMING THE WILDERNESS

Among the wooded hills of the Appalachians a group of little rivers rise in western Virginia and North Carolina and northern Georgia; they flow into the Tennessee River in Tennessee and the valley extends into Alabama and then back through Tennessee and Kentucky to empty into the Ohio River. In the floods of

1937 the raging waters of the Ohio and most of its tributaries wrought havoc throughout the Ohio River watershed. Metropolitan districts were paralyzed and whole towns were forced to flee. Destruction of life and property was very great and suffering throughout the area was intense.

But there was an exception to this story of widespread grief and horror. The people of the Tennessee Valley knew no hardship; their homes were not engulfed and swept away by the relentless torrents, and for them the floods, which held the regions all about them in terror, were remote indeed. The modern wonder which kept this valley safe while other valleys suffered was engineering. An integrated system of great dams separates the Tennessee Valley into a series of great lakes held by the power-producing dams. Far up the stream on the Clinch River the chain begins with the mighty Norris Dam, not far from the city of Knoxville, Tennessee. Below it are others, some projected, some under construction. Farther down the stream are the Wilson and Wheeler Dams, creating a great lake which stretches back for more than eighty-six miles.

A CONCRETE RIB IN THE ROCK-RIBBED HILLS

Stretching across the green valley of the Clinch River, a mass of concrete from hill to hill, the Norris Dam holds back a great lake extending for forty-seven miles up the Clinch and Powell rivers. In this heroic project the co-operation of the engineering brotherhood was dramatically demonstrated. The electrical engineers provided the civil engineers with power so that the civil engineers could build a dam to furnish electricity for the electrical engineers. Men of a dozen other branches of engineering aided in the undertaking, specialists in hydraulics, construction, chemistry, efficiency, transportation, forestry, housing, and many others. In three years twenty-seven million feet of concrete were poured to make the gigantic dam. For almost a third of a mile the sloping white expanse extends, a sleeping giant, across the valley, who preserves the region around him from flood and erosion and supplies

NORRIS DAM
SPILLWAYS ARE
40 FEET HIGHER
THAN NIAGARA

TVA photo

it with electric lights and fertilizer. And this giant is the creation of the engineers, here as always—planning, charting, testing each step taken in achieving the whole.

TWO HUNDRED FEET OF CONCRETE AGAINST THE WATER

All but three hundred feet of the length of the dam is a giant concrete slab which tapers from the amazing thickness of 204 feet in the river bed to a roadway along the top, 265 feet above the foundation. The three-hundred-foot extension at the eastern end of the dam is a massive earthwork with a concrete core. From the level of the three great one-hundred-foot spillways, which are thirty-one feet below the roadway, powerful emergency gates can operate in times of flood to control water levels to within a few feet of the crest of the dam. These mighty flood gates are hydraulically operated steel drums; when flood begins to reach higher and higher on the walls of the dam, threatening the lives of the people who live in the valley below, the dam girds itself with the armor of these supplementary gates.

As the Norris Project is only part of the great Tennessee Valley system, so the Norris Dam is only a part of the local project. Along the shores of Norris Lake other activities are carried on— fire prevention, malarial control measures, soil erosion control, forestry and reforestation, housing projects, and road construction.

Nestled against the downstream slope of the dam is the power house. In it are two great generators operated by a pair of turbines. Each of these giant turbines develops sixty-six thousand horse-power to turn the generators, and the generators produce the electricity which flows out through the marching power lines to the homes and factories of the entire region. It is in projects like this great dam and its power plant that engineers furnish power to the world, the power which their brother engineers in other fields apply to motors and lights, furnaces and communication.

When the generators of electricity were developed which could produce current in large enough amounts to be worth while sending out to distant points, a new set of problems was laid before the engineers. How can the transmission be accomplished with the least loss of power and the greatest economy in installation and maintenance of transmission apparatus? The engineers took the question and went back to their diagrams and graphs of conductivity and strength of materials. When the diagrams and graphs were incomplete or apparently offered no help they made new ones from new experiments.

They learned that efficient long-distance transmission of electricity is best done by utilizing alternating current at very high voltages. In order to do this the engineers designed mighty transformers by which the voltage is stepped up when it enters the high tension lines and then stepped down at the points where it is to be used. Given the kind of power which they were to transmit, the engineers set about to perfect a medium through which it could be sent efficiently. It had to be heavy enough to ride securely through wind storms, yet light enough to be carried from the cross arms of lofty towers. It had to be flexible but not too flexible. Maximum conductivity was necessary as was great strength. Insulation which could withstand the shattering voltages the cables were to carry was essential. Consulting their charts the engineers began experiments, pulling and twisting and pounding wires and subjecting their metals and other substances to staggering amounts of electricity. They tried out copper strands and wires of aluminum and steel and combinations of the three. They insulated their wires with a variety of materials and sheathed them in lead and hemp and specially treated paper. They covered the cables with steel armor and went on to other problems that surged into their path when a good conductor had been created.

DANGER—A QUARTER OF A MILLION VOLTS

The next problem confronting the engineers was that of finding a way to carry their high tension lines from place to place. The cables were like flowing dynamite; whatever grounded them —man or beast or tree or building—would be seared to a blackened cinder by the touch. Engineers planted the cables underground and devised ways of preventing water erosion, leakage into the ground and the ravages of insects living beneath the surface of the earth. Finding in many cases that the difficulties of maintaining this type of cable, its inaccessibility and liability to underground destruction made the apparatus impractical, the engineers began to experiment with hanging the lines high in the air, out of reach of all things to which the electricity might bring annihilation.

Engineers drew plans and tested models of great towers and chains of hanging insulators. The simple wooden poles and cup insulators of telephone lines seem simple indeed when contrasted with the products of these experiments. High tension towers rise as high as one hundred and fifty feet in the air. They are made of steel, four-cornered tapering giants constructed with massive girders, and their cross bars are the outstretched arms of titans.

The insulators from which the heavy cables hang like spider webs, high in the air, are many feet apart on the cross arms to prevent any leakage or short circuit. The lines are in constant danger of destruction by lightning or high winds, and they are protected by elaborate lightning rod devices and supported by construction so strong that it makes the suspension of small and low distribution wires seem puny and frail indeed.

Spanning rivers, leaping chasms, silently marching across hill and valley, mountain and plain, the great high tension towers holding aloft their precious burden of power are fit tributes to the engineers, the men of science who build them.

ELECTRICITY PUNCHES THE TIME CLOCK

From the generators of the great dams and waterfalls, through the cables of the high tension lines, the power of electricity comes to work. It enters factories and shops, lighting plants and mills, the servant of industry which answers the pressure of a fingertip on a button to do the work which a thousand fingertips or arms or shoulders could not do. Here the current flows into electro-magnets which can lift tons upon tons of iron ingots, there it streams into the cold coils which turn ponderous motors or the searing, red hot coils of blast furnaces which turn huge loads of ore into seething cauldrons of molten metal, and in still another place it takes on the voice of a single, clear-throated flute or the mighty singing of a great symphony and sends it out across the air and into the fireside radios of millions of homes. Guiding its surging power is the engineer, adjusting the dials in broadcast control rooms, planning, designing, building, and maintaining the electro-magnets and motors and furnaces.

HOOKING UP THE COAST-TO-COAST HOOK-UP

The radio industry is a helpless thing, a useless mob of musicians and actors and writers and accountants, without the electrical engineer. The shrillest soprano could sing her loudest, the most popular comedian could jest his best, but if the electric power failed, the voices would play to empty rooms and the radio, which has become a national institution, would be merely a quiet piece of furniture. The electrical engineer has constructed a microphone so sensitive that the echoing of the best designed studio is caught and distorts the voices of the violins and the contraltos. The engineer who planned the studio acoustics has done his best and it has been good enough in concert halls and auditoriums, but in the broadcasting studio perfect acoustics is not enough.

The chemical engineers set to work to perfᴖct soundproof and non-reflecting walls. They created fabrics and tested bricks, molded tiles and ground up wood. The modern studio, their eventual achievement, is surrounded by walls nearly two feet in thickness. These complex walls are built of layer upon layer of hollow tiling, fabricated board, and sheeting of other chemically manufactured materials. The surface is porous, punctured in

Courtesy National Broadcasting Company

RECEPTION OF "NARROWCASTING" MESSAGES FROM THE DIRIGIBLE
LOS ANGELES AT LAKEHURST, N. J.

myriad holes which absorb the drifting waves of sound and leave the microphone free to receive each successive note and syllable and breath in its original clarity of tone.

"MIKE," THE PATIENT LISTENER

The microphone eternally listens to the wares of the radio artist, lending the ear of his condenser to good music and bad, to comedy and commercial announcements, to the latest news and the oldest drama. "Mike" listens unemotionally to all sounds and transforms them into impulses which flow through wires to the vacuum tube oscillators of radio station transmitters. Radio is still a new industry, and the engineers who have pioneered its development are still making great strides.

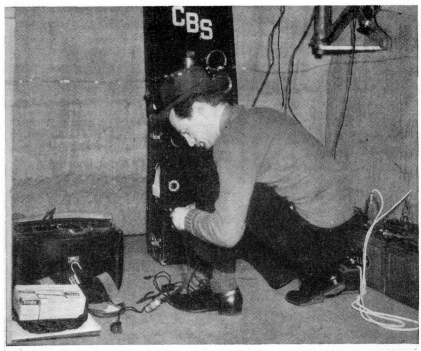

Courtesy Columbia Broadcasting System

PREPARING TO BROADCAST FROM WASHINGTON MONUMENT
Engineer installing ultra high frequency relay broadcast transmitter at top of monument, for use in presidential inaugural broadcast.

The transmitting station pours the electrical sound waves into a beam of electromagnetic waves which flow at a specific frequency out into the air and across the world. The crest-to-crest distance is called the wave length and as the length of the wave increases its frequency of flux decreases. Each radio station has its own frequency and corresponding wave length, in a range which extends from the short wave transmitters of many foreign stations, amateurs who are called "hams," and police squad cars, to the powerful, commercially operated stations. Streaming through the air are also the dot and dash signals of airplane pilots and of the thousands of "Sparks"—the ship radio men. Electromagnetic radio waves carried the messages of the Byrd expedition from the ice-bound wastes of the South Pole, as well as the strange notes of the crooners. These magic vibrations flying through the air have made possible the amazing "blind flying" which has contributed so much to the safety of modern aviation. Remote control of airplanes and ships is a further astounding development which the engineers have given to the world. Operated by a

Paul's Photos, Chicago

PILOT'S COCKPIT OF A RADIO-EQUIPPED MAIL PLANE

Courtesy United Air Lines

DIAGRAM SHOWING HOW A PLANE IS GUIDED IN FLIGHT
BY RADIO BEACONS

man twirling dials at a desk miles away, planes piloted by remote control soar high above mountains and land flawlessly after their seemingly impossible flights.

S-O-S, . . . — — . . .

Electrical engineers have also given to air transportation the radio compass and the directional radio beam, giving man greater and greater power over the sleet storms and blinding fogs of nature, making air travel and flying almost foolproof. It was in ships that the first applications of radio transmission were made, and the ship's radio engineer has become a traditionally heroic figure, tirelessly tapping out his messages. In shipwreck and disaster the living cargo of the ship is in his hands, and with the captain he sticks with the ship to the end, desperately sending out the S-O-S signal which may result in the saving of hundreds of lives.

Radio renders other, less stirringly dramatic, services to the men of the sea and air. Coast guard and other craft wireless the location of icebergs and wheather hazards in travel lanes to coast guard stations so that a general alarm may be sounded when these frozen giants begin to roam the seas in the spring. Farming has been affected greatly by the broadcasting of farm commodity market prices. Education and particularly musical education, has been both aided and stimulated by the transmission of radio programs. Back of these and many other services stands an engineer, supervising present radio processes and techniques and devising improvements in them. His efforts are making the production of practical and economical television apparatus an inevitable event.

In the creation, maintenance, and improvement of modern material civilization there are few groups which are more vitally important than the electrical engineers. Wielding a force which has never been defined and which no one has ever seen, the engineer painstakingly and skilfully conducts the great source of power with which he deals from its generation to its numberless ultimate uses. His genius has converted an unknown quantity into the most productive tool which man has ever known. But he is not satisfied with that; he helps the physicist and chemist in the researches which are reaching out toward greater and greater sources of energy. He is awaiting and speeding the invention of a means to utilize the vast latent power which is hidden in the atom. He longs to work out applications of this hidden energy, which is so great that if the atom-splitting process could be applied to one pail of water, enough power could be furnished to drive a great ship across the seas. He looks forward into the future and attempts to use the power of the sun, the tides, and the intense heat of the core of the earth.

THE ENGINEER WITH A STOP WATCH

There is another great group of engineers engaged in building the machine age. These are the efficiency engineers, the production engineers, the planners of organization, management and personnel, who speed processes by inventing time- and labor-saving devices and methods. Following through the work of their colleagues who labor with energy sources and materials, the production engineers combine these two, designing and building machines to use them in the manufacture of the thousands of products of modern engineering. Here too is human engineering, the co-ordinating of people in the operation of these machines, and the stimulation of efficiency in both machines and men. Their criterion of success is output, measured and counted; every step of each process is timed and timed again, and it is up to the engineers to see that industrial output and its speed and efficiency are always on the increase. Engineers work with intangibles. Their work is often concerned with things which they cannot see. Chemical engineers guide and control the action of atoms and even electrons, although none of them has ever seen one. Electrical engineers solve problems and move mountains with a force which is indefinable. In a like way the productive efficiency engineer deals with time. He, like the others, can see the results, the product of the forces he works with, but his actual struggle is with invisible, yet relentless and ever-moving, time.

The production engineers are truly scientific in their work of increasing the efficiency of industry. In their research they reduce to the simplest forms the problems intrusted to them. Their experiments hold constant all but one of these elements, and by varying the one factor they are able to see its individual influence on the process as a whole. Thus when the problem of improving

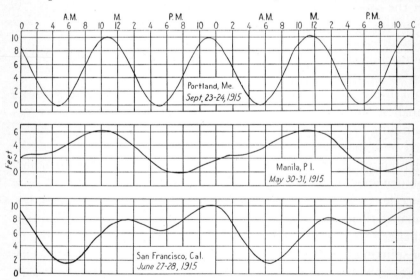

Courtesy Coast and Geodetic Survey, U. S. Dept. of Commerce

HOURLY GRAPHS OF THREE TYPES OF TIDES
This chart shows the technical way in which engineers record tidal movements.
The graphs are produced automatically on timed drums.

the efficiency of a belt, driven by a motor and turning the shaft of a machine, is given to an engineer, he considers the performance of the belt from the separate standpoints of materials, tension, friction, vibration, optimum speed, and the like. He varies the tension of the belt, holding all the other factors the same. He tests machine output when the belt is very tight; then he loosens it very slightly and tests again. He repeats the operation again and again until the belt is so loose that it begins to slip, and then he makes his graph which tells him at what point the belt is most efficient. This decided, he takes up another factor, testing and checking it until the entire machine is at its production peak.

EFFICIENCY MADE TO ORDER

Factory owners, industrialists, and promoters came to engineers with their problems. They wanted the wheels to turn faster. They wanted the wheels to turn more efficiently. They wanted money changed into raw materials and raw materials turned into finished products—automobiles, cash-registers, or coffee pots—in the shortest possible time. The engineers took up the task of planning a factory process in the same methodical way as they would have tackled the job of creating a new alloy for airplane motors or a new cheese to satisfy the taste of the public. They busied themselves with sketches and slide rules, with blueprints and logarithms. They split up a factory process into all its smallest successive stages; they analyzed the various steps in assembling an automobile from the casting of the first connecting rod and the punching out of the first spring leaf down to the tightening of the last bolt and the application of the final line of ornamental gilt. In this way they created a kind of jigsaw puzzle; as soon as they surveyed each part of the puzzle they turned their wits to reassembling it. In doing this they often changed the component individual parts, combining two into one or splitting one into two. They played a game of chess with workmen, raw materials, half-finished parts, and factory buildings. They deployed their pieces strategically; they rearranged the order of their pawns, sometimes jumping one over another; occasionally they even changed the size and shape of the chessboard itself—

that is, the size and shape of the factory floor. Against such over-whelming tactics, waste and delay had no chance. The engineers won the game.

One of the most difficult strategic problems in this game was the moving of parts and materials from workman to workman and from machine to machine. Previously, the workmen themselves had to shuttle back and forth, carrying the parts on to the next man when they were through with them. Even if the parts were light in weight this involved an interruption and waste of time; if they were heavy it demanded backbreaking efforts; if they were so heavy that they could not be moved readily, the workmen had to bustle about and come to the object to do their particular jobs.

To solve this problem at one stroke the engineers devised the idea of the moving conveyor, a mechanical servant to fetch and carry for the workmen and the machines. This servant had its birth in grist mills and foundries where bucket-chains were used to carry flour, and belts were used to transport molding sand. It grew to manhood in the automobile assembling plants. Today belts and slides and series of trucks are winding their serpentine ways through all sorts of factories. Over busy work benches move endless chains; on these chains are little hooks; on the hooks hang the objects going through the process of manufacture. Motors for electric fans are assembled in this fashion. The workman unhooks a motor, puts in a special screw or affixes an enameled base, then hooks it on again—but not on the same hook, for the chain keeps moving.

GLASS BOTTLES MARCH

Among the many interesting products that conveyors slide through factories and plants are the 10,000,000,000 bottles containing carbonated beverages Americans drink annually. Into the plant goes an endless line of them; some are empties returning from drug stores and grocery shops; some come fresh from automatic multiple glass-blowing machines, another monument to the engineers of mass production. Some of the bottles are chipped and worn, some are new and glistening; some bear the torn remains of old labels; some have no labels at all. Like a caravan of

Courtesy U. S. Bottlers Machinery Co., Chicago

STERILIZING AND WASHING MECHANISM IN A DISTILLERY

glass soldiers they slide along. First they go to the soaking and washing machines and the air washers, where they are held firmly in little individual nests to prevent breakage; out of the air washer they are gently tipped in squads of eight on another belt, whose fence-like sides prevent them from upsetting. Their next visit is to the mechanical taps which measure out the right amount of syrup—strawberry, lemon, orange, or ginger—more precisely and methodically than can be done by human hand. Then on to the pressure fillers to get their quota of carbonated water; then continuing to the capping machine which tops them with an airtight crown. All along the way mechanical arms grasp and steady them. Their progress through the plant is like a great marionette show, with a few operators holding the strings. Finally the filled bottles break ranks and form squads in cartons and cases, which are moved by still other rolling conveyors to waiting trucks and trains.

The synchronized march of the pop bottles is impressive in itself; however, each step in that march shows the handiwork of the engineer. The cork-lined metal caps that are snugly clamped around the mouths of the bottles and the cleverly shaped cardboard cartons are themselves the product of mechanical ingenuity and efficiency. As we survey other industries this fact becomes even more apparent. In the making of automobiles, there is not only the final assembly line, which builds a skeleton chassis up to a thing of glistening, streamlined beauty; there are also the subordinate lines that build up the motor, the body, the springs, the radiator. Furthermore, the moving conveyors that carry motor and springs along the subordinate lines are also fed with small parts by still other conveyors!

An automobile assembly plant is like a tree: raw materials are fed in at the ends of the twigs to make the smallest parts; these twigs combine into the branches and limbs which represent the major parts of the car; finally the limbs and branches join in making up the trunk—the finished product. Furthermore, each twig and branch also represents a moving conveyor. Obviously the speeds of these various conveyors are of great importance. They must move slowly enough for each separate operation to be performed along the line; if the line is to be speeded up *every* worker must work faster; therefore it is essential that the various operations be split up in such a way that each takes the same time to perform. Moreover, if one subordinate line works faster than another, there is no gain. Perhaps the swiftest line is that one that builds motors. What happens? Motors pile up; room has to be found for them; they represent money that is tied up and not in motion. It is only the speed of the assembly plant as a whole that makes for profit; individual speed does not contribute greatly to profits. The engineer must regulate the speed of each workman and each machine in the same way as an orchestra leader directs the tempo of each woodwind, string, and brass. Having devised the conveyors, it has become his problem to see that they are efficiently used. He must take the grinding wheels of industry and make of them a carefully timed symphony.

THE ELECTRIC EYE—SEES ALL, KNOWS NOTHING

Another of the outstanding developments in labor-saving techniques involves the use of the photoelectric cell, better known as the electric eye. This cell was a gadget devised by physicists, and its development for use in industrial processes is one of the greatest triumphs of the production engineers. The cell in its early forms was not extremely sensitive. It registered simple variations in the degree of light, such as the difference in light reflected by a tin can and the belt on which it moved. The cell did this by emitting a small electric current whose strength was governed by the varying amount of light which reached its sensitive surface. These early electric eyes could be used for counting, and as counters they were very valuable. They were more accurate and more dependable than the human eye, for they never looked away momentarily and lost count, nor did they grow weary and suffer blurred sight.

But this time- and labor-saving device was only the crude beginning from which the engineers developed the electric eye which performs a thousand diverse and difficult tasks in industrial processes. The sensitivity of the cell was vastly increased until it could register more minute variations in color than could the human eye. Its range of uses was immensely broadened by this ability, and to counting was added the more difficult and important work of sorting. The cell is more rapid than the human eye, and with the introduction of photoelectricity, machine production which had previously been slowed to the rate of human inspectors could expand to the maximum efficient speed of the machine itself. The first electric eyes had been able to "see" an automobile approaching a crossing and act to change the traffic lights, but the highly developed modern cells can differentiate between grades of lubricating oil. To the work of the older type of cell in counting cans and department store customers were added new duties. In the industrial world of today photoelectric cells are used to sort tiny variations in the thickness of paper, to pull metal ingots from blast furnaces when their shade of red indicates that they have reached a desired heat, and to throw out defective bottles and ball bearings. Work which was merely a deadly routine and a waste of human ability and energy was turned by the electric eye into a rapid and efficient engineering advance integral in and worthy of the machine age.

THE HUMAN FACTOR

But the industries of the world asked for more than mere mechanical innovation and improvement. They needed human engineering. Workers were studied as they performed their tasks. The engineers made motion pictures of factory employees at their work, sometimes attaching little lights to their fingers, in an effort to eliminate every erg of wasted energy. Time studies of fatigue, working hours, and recreation or relaxation intervals were compiled and studied, and engineers discovered that with a shorter working day individual output was often increased. Personnel engineers called psychoanalysts to their aid, and by using interviews and questionnaires the hiring of workers was made a scientific procedure. Scientific hiring does away with much maladjustment and consequent inefficiency, and discharge for incompetence is less frequent.

Armed with charts and graphs the efficiency engineer approached the problems of management. He introduced careful methods of inventory, and his studies of obsolescence made purchasing of machinery and systematic replacement of factory buildings an important part of modern management. The functions of the budget, the pre-audit, the audit, and scientific accounting were brought to bear on industry, reducing waste, eliminating mistakes and haphazard guessing. The engineer followed the products of industry beyond the factory and workshop. He studied jobbing, wholesaling, retailing, and advertising methods with an eye to their economic soundness, asking and getting facts —facts proved by figures and verified in research.

Engineers are everywhere in the modern industrial world, changing the face of the earth and building the most impressive material civilization the world has ever known. They are a heroic guild, pioneering their anonymous way into the mists of the impossible, turning inconceivable dreams into accomplished facts. Men of genius and creative imagination, they add to the highly specialized technical training of the great engineering schools their years of patient and unpraised research and experiment. In their world of material creation they are the true moderns.

THE ENGINEERING OF MATERIALS

THE IMPORTANCE OF MATERIALS

TO AN ENGINEER materials are of utmost importance: they are the very fabric of industry. Great are their numbers and variety, for to the materials that occur in nature the products of laboratory and foundry have been added.

Often the engineer has taken two or more substances and combined them chemically or mechanically to produce still another type, which may adapt itself to new and revolutionary uses. An excellent example is concrete, formed when men mix sand, water, cement, and a suitable coarse aggregate, usually crushed rock. The use of concrete has revolutionized road and building construction. Paint, a combination of oils and pigments, is another example; it gives valuable service by protecting outside surfaces against the destructive effects of the elements.

How strong is steel? What are the best types of steel for a particular construction project? What effect will traffic have on the surface of a concrete pavement? How waterproof is an asphalt roofing material? These are vital problems that concern the construction engineer. He must know the physical properties of every structural part, and must determine the proper materials to sustain the loads that will bear upon them.

No less important is the economic phase of the engineer's knowledge of building materials. He must give this phase just as much attention as any other. To build the most efficient structure he must use only the amount of material necessary, and not just put in about ten more columns to make sure the building will stand up. He must concern himself with margins of safety, with stresses and strains.

These and other complex features of modern construction methods have made it necessary to adopt a code of standards governing the use of materials and characteristics.

To this end the United States Bureau of Standards was created by Act of Congress in 1901. The purpose of this organization is

TESTING MA-CHINE FOR CON-CRETE AND STEEL
This machine makes compression tests on concrete, and tensile strength, yield point and elongation tests on steel and other metals. It registers up to 200,000 lbs.

Courtesy Walter H. Flood & Co.

to make available all the necessary knowledge about building materials, and to determine their physical constants, their weight, strength, elasticity, power to resist corrosion, and so on. The Bureau protects its standard units of weight and measurement, its yardsticks and scales with extreme caution. Varying atmospheric conditions make it essential that they be safeguarded from expansion and contraction, and from picking up foreign substances that would cause variation in weight. This watchfulness is important because the Bureau's standards are used for calibrating weighing and measuring instruments that are in daily use. They are the yardsticks of yardsticks, the scales of scales, the last court of appeal in the realm of measures and weights.

The rod on which is marked the standard inch is particularly guarded against temperature change, to prevent any possibility of expansion or contraction, that would result in erroneous calibrations of other measuring instruments. Some of the extremely light weights used in setting scales and balances cannot be touched by human hands, because perspiration might double their weight. The Bureau of Standard's units of weight and length are stored in a fireproof, air-tight vault. Many of them were manufactured by the Bureau International, in Sèvres, France.

From time to time the Bureau publishes bulletins setting forth the results of tests and investigations that have been made. These are a valuable source of information for the engineer, for they tell him of new materials or new processes that have been found advantageous. The facilities of the Bureau are available to engineers and scientists, enabling them to check their standards against those Congress has declared to be official. The vaults of the Bureau guard the standard units—the perfect yardstick, the perfect pound weight, and other similar units—as if they were the rarest treasures on earth.

There is still another agency which will give the engineer the information he desires concerning certain work, and which also furnishes a set of standards recognized by the engineering profession. This is the American Society for Testing Materials. This society was organized as an American section of the International Association for Testing Materials, which was established in 1895. The American section had its origin in Philadelphia in 1898, and has standardized the work of the engineer to a considerable degree. Its official purpose is "the promotion of knowledge of the materials of engineering and the standardization of specifications and methods of tests."

The 4,200 members of the American Society for Testing Materials are divided into three classes: producers of raw, semi-finished, and finished materials; commercial users of materials; and other interested groups, such as educators, consulting engineers, and scientists. The work of research, investigation, and testing is carried on by the members of the various groups. It is usually done in the laboratories of the companies and organizations that are especially interested in the work under investigation. The cunning of individual industrial workers is tapped in order to help all industry.

Through the years of experience of engineers, builders, architects, and others, certain fundamental knowledge has been accumulated. Analysis of this knowledge has revealed certain relationships from which can be formulated concise statements or laws governing each case. The collection of these fundamentals or laws and the mathematical treatment of them has formed the basis of a new engineering science—the study of the strength of materials.

THE STRENGTH OF MATERIALS

When the engineer has designed his building and determined the loads that must be carried, he must choose his materials, keeping in mind his special problems. Some are incapable of supporting the loads required of his structures; others can support the loads but are uneconomical or impractical; only a few are exactly suited. The two previously mentioned agencies help the engineer to find those he needs.

The term "strength of materials" itself undoubtedly creates the thought of how much pull a rope or cable can stand before breaking. In the construction of a concrete pavement, for example, the highway engineer must know the type of concrete that will withstand the loads of the heaviest vehicle that can possibly travel over it. Great expense and inconvenience will result if he lays concrete of less strength than is necessary.

Just as there are technical terms in almost every other occupation in life, there are terms peculiar to the study of the strength of materials. It might be well to discuss some of them and their significance.

"Stress" is one of the principal terms used in discussing strength of materials. This is a measure of the amount of unit pressure which a material can withstand. This pressure may be either a pull (tension), or push or squeeze (compression). If, for example, a vertical bar of one square inch cross-sectional area is supporting a weight of 1,000 pounds, the bar must exert an equal pressure to keep from being pulled apart. Since the 1,000 pounds acts over an area of one square inch in our illustration, the unit pressure, or stress, is 1,000 pounds per square inch. For bodies of different area, the unit stress is determined by dividing the total weight by the cross-sectional area. If the bar were four square inches in area, the unit stress would be 250 pounds per square inch. Similarly, if a body is squeezed, or compressed, the pressure divided by the area over which it acts will give the amount of unit stress.

Another important term is "strain." It pertains to the stretching qualities or elasticity of a material, such as steel, iron, or wood. Rubber is commonly thought of as an elastic substance, but the truth of the matter is that steel is more elastic, because, within certain limits, it is capable of returning to its original shape upon the release of the pressure or load which caused it to stretch. Rubber, on the other hand, does not resume its precise original size and shape under such circumstances.

Of course the stretching of steel is not visible under ordinary conditions. It may be seen, however, when the strength of steel is tested to the point of destruction. In such a test, one of the facts sought is the point beyond which the stretched steel will not return to its original shape. This is called the "elastic limit," and is accompanied by a visible, sudden stretching of the metal. Very little additional pressure is necessary beyond this point to pull the specimen in two.

The elastic limit of metals varies to a considerable degree. That of bronze wire, for example, may be between 8,000 and 16,000 pounds per square inch while steel alloys may vary from 50,000 to 90,000 pounds per square inch, or even higher. The elastic limit of copper wire has been determined by a countless number of tests as falling between 14,000 and 16,000 pounds per square inch. These figures are important to an engineer who is constructing a high power transmission line. He wants to know if the wire will be able to support its own weight and any loads that may be imposed on it, such as the weight of ice and the pressure of high winds. Ordinary steel has an elastic limit ranging between 25,000 and 35,000 pounds per square inch. These figures, as pointed out before, are not the values at which these materials will break, but beyond which they will not be in an elastic state.

The composition of various metals and other building materials and the methods for their use, are specified by the American Society for Testing Materials. This information simplifies greatly the engineer's task. It gives him more time for better designing, since he knows he will be able to find accurate information about the material his particular job requires. He does not have to waste time investigating whether or not a steel rod will carry a certain load if he knows that the manufacturer has made that piece according to standard specifications, and has also performed the necessary tests.

A FLY CAN BEND A STEEL BAR

Although the words that have just been described, "stress" and "strain," usually mean the same thing to the layman, they have a special significance to the engineer. Their determination has demanded the invention and development of very precise machines, which have made the quality of building materials better. With suitable instruments, the engineer or investigator can measure the sag of a steel beam regardless of the amount of the load that is applied to it. The capabilities of these machines are illustrated by one that is used by the United States Bureau of Standards. It has a two-inch steel bar clamped to it in cantilever fashion. By means of light waves and a very powerful telescope it is possible to observe the amount of deflection the steel bar undergoes when only a fly alights on the free end!

Returning again to the comparison between rubber and steel, an important difference may be noted in the manner in which they stretch. For example, if a rubber band stretches two inches with the application of a one-pound pull, it will stretch more than another two inches if another pound pull be applied. In other words, each time the pull is increased by one pound the piece of rubber will stretch a little more in proportion to the amount it did the previous time. Such a condition is not true, however, in regard to the stretching characteristics of steel. Suppose, for example, a 100-pound pull stretches a steel wire 1/1,000 of an inch, each additional 100-pound pull will stretch it an equal amount. Moreover, when the pull is lessened, the steel will return to its original shape, provided it was not stretched beyond its elastic limit. Because of this fact, the engineer considers steel to be a perfectly elastic substance. Rubber is not so considered. Truly speaking, rubber is plastic rather than elastic. All this apparently theoretical and experimental work with elastic substances has a very practical application. Handbooks containing this information are of inestimable assistance to the construction engineer.

The new Golden Gate suspension bridge in San Francisco is supported by cables composed of steel wires about the thickness of a pencil. Thousands of these wires are bundled tightly together into a bulky cable three and one-half feet in diameter. One would not ordinarily think of such a huge bundle of steel wire stretching very much. Yet, it is a fact that when the bridge is fully loaded, these cables are capable of stretching 23 feet. This may be illustrated by another experiment. If, for example, a steel bar one inch square has hung from it a weight of 1,000 pounds, it will stretch 1/29,000 of an inch. Comparatively speaking, that is not very much, but in a structure as large as a bridge or tall building, the consequent amount of stretch is a problem that must be given very close attention. Skyscrapers and other mammoth structures present difficulties all their own.

Steel is one of the strongest structural materials we have; that is why the engineer uses it to erect the huge edifices that now characterize our great cities. However, the engineer does not avail himself of the great possibilities that this material possesses when he designs a structure. As mentioned before, a bar of steel of one square inch cross sectional area can support from seventeen to forty-five tons of weight before it fails, but the engineer would not dare to base his calculations on this figure and provide merely the amount that would be absolutely necessary to carry the load of the masonry. Instead he leaves a "margin of safety," so that unnoticed flaws or unusual natural forces, such as earthquakes and great storms, will not wreck his structure. In the case of steel, he would not impose loads on a structural member that would exceed half the amount he knows the steel will carry. In the case of the bar with a cross section of one square inch, the engineer would not load it with a stress of more than 8 to 20 tons. Should the load be greater than this, even though it still falls within the maximum strength of the single bar, he would provide for the addition of one or more extra bars.

STRONG AS STEEL

Consider a heavily loaded truck weighing seventeen tons. Actually it takes very little steel to support this load, but everyone is familiar with the strong metal framework that is used in the construction of a truck, which is much more than is actually required. The added amount provides a margin of safety to take care of any emergency that may arise. But even after allowing for a margin of safety modern steel remains prodigiously strong, as was vividly illustrated in an exhibit at the Chicago Century of Progress Exposition. The feature of this particular exhibit was the suspension of the dead weight of three automobiles from a single wire automobile wheel, which could have held several more automobiles, had there been room for them.

The steel framework of a monster skyscraper carries the entire weight of the structure including all the reinforced concrete and masonry as well as all the fixtures and all the people that use the building. Were it not for the capabilities of steel, huge skyscrapers would be impractical, and the construction of eighty-storied buildings would be an impossibility. One of the most striking examples of this fact is the edifice whose sheer mass and hugeness amaze all who see it—the Empire State Building in New York City. This gigantic structure is 1,250 feet high—almost a quarter of a mile into the Manhattan sky. Its construction even includes a mooring mast for dirigibles. Had this building been constructed of concrete and masonry, it is very possible that the columns, especially those on the lower floors, would have been of such tremendous size that they would have taken up all the room, leaving at best only narrow passages between. Even then it would probably have toppled down before it was half-built. There are any number of other great skyscrapers throughout the country whose construction would have been equally impractical had it not been possible to use the various kinds of steel that the modern construction engineer has at his disposal.

San Francisco's Golden Gate bridge would not have been feasible had not steel been used in its construction. Each of its towers consists of two columns which rest on the bridge piers, supporting the entire structure whose clear span is 4,200 feet, the longest in the world. Each column contains 12,500 square

Courtesy San Francisco Chamber of Commerce
THE GOLDEN GATE BRIDGE AT SAN FRANCISCO

inches of steel—almost nine square feet. This steel is shaped in various angles, plates, and channels, built up in cell construction. The enormous weight that the 700-foot towers are able to support, amounts to 43,000 tons, which is approximately the weight of the largest battleship afloat, and comparable to the weight of that super-liner, the *Queen Mary*.

A unique problem solved in a no less unique manner presented itself in the copper mining country in northern Michigan. Some of the mine shafts are about 6,000 feet deep, and it is more economical to hoist the ore from the mine in one stage, rather than lift it in a series of hoists from level to level. It was made possible to lift the ore in a single operation by the introduction of steel wire of tapered construction. The wire is thicker at the top than it is at the bottom. The reason for shaping a wire thus lies in the fact that the cable must support its own weight in addition to the weight of the ore and the carriage. The amount of the weight of the cable in comparison to the weight of the entire load may be better appreciated when it is realized that a one-inch steel cable of sufficient length to reach to the bottom of the mine shaft would weigh about 18,000 pounds or nine tons, which is about half the load it could safely lift. It would be dangerous and uneconomical to go beyond the safe limit; yet in this case such would have to be done if the cable were of uniform thickness all the way along its length. A tapered construction provides the necessary strength at the top without greatly increasing the total weight of the cable. Pay-loads of ore can be lifted out of the depths of earth in a single hoist.

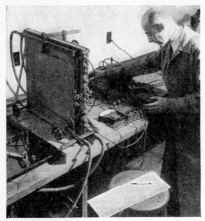

Courtesy *Armour Engineer and Alumnus*

TESTING INSULATION WITH FLAT
PLATE CONDUCTOR

CONDUCTIVITY

The engineer, in the design and construction of a building in particular, has another problem that he must take into account. This is one of heating, and the methods of most economical and effective types of heating present an entire field of engineering that is rapidly becoming more and more important in construction work. It is not hard to realize that, if we try to heat a building and the walls do not retain the heat, a more vigorous fire will be necessary and this will only run up the fuel bill without giving any satisfaction. This "heating the outdoors," as it is sometimes called, is combated by various means. One method that is attaining great popularity is the process of insulation. This means that a material is placed in the walls of a building that will not allow the passage of the heat into the outside air. The effectiveness of insulation may be better realized if we discuss the behavior of the molecules of a substance.

All bodies of the universe emit ether waves because of the vibration of the molecules that compose them. The wave lengths of these molecular vibrations vary from .00002 of a centimeter to a few hundredths of a millimeter. These waves carry energy, and the absorption of this energy by another body results in its dissipation in the form of heat. Some substances absorb these energy waves very readily, and others do not. Hence, those bodies that readily absorb these waves cause a transfer of heat, and are poor material to use in insulating a building, because they transmit all the heat through the walls into the outside air. The engineer therefore strives to find and use materials that are not good conductors of heat. This will mean that a lesser amount of heat will be necessary, thus cutting down the amount of fuel that need be used. Metals, as a rule, are good conductors of heat, but the engineer cannot entirely sacrifice their use because their strength is very desirable. He has to use another material in conjunction with the structural metal, a material that will retain the heat of the building. Rock-wool is a substance that is widely used in insulating walls, as are different types of fibrous materials. Their installation can be accomplished either by applying the insulating material in layers to the inside of a wall or by blowing it in by compressed air. The wide application of these wood and cloth insulating materials is due to the engineer's knowledge that they are poor conductors of heat, a knowledge gleaned from many experiments.

The molecular theory of conductivity may be further illustrated by the heating of a long metal rod at one end to a much higher temperature than the other end. After a short time it will be noticed that the cooler end becomes warm. This is because the hot end is sending its heat along the length of the rod from molecule to molecule. A transfer of heat is not possible unless there is a difference in temperature between two bodies. This is the same as saying that water will not flow unless there be a difference of elevation between two bodies of water. Unless one be higher than the other, there is no place for the water of either body to flow.

Polished materials and even some metals do not readily absorb heat waves, but they reflect them; hence they cannot easily be heated. In hot countries all the buildings are commonly made of white materials. This is because a white body, like a polished one, will not readily absorb heat waves. White clothes are worn in summer for the same reason. Hardly anyone of us would think of going about in hot weather with a black suit or dress, because we know, though we may not know why, that we will become unbearably warm. So we change to light clothes, both as to color and weight, in an effort to escape the heat of the atmosphere.

The construction of a miner's safety lamp uses the theory of conduction to safeguard the miner from any possibility of his light igniting gases that may be present in the mine. The heat rising from the flame in his lamp hits a wire gauze envelope which is a good conductor of heat. Hence, much of the heat from the flame is dissipated by the wire gauze, reducing the amount which reaches the outside air. Such a low temperature will not ignite any gas that might be present in combustible quantities.

STABILITY

Stability must be included in the list of important items that an engineer has to consider in planning a structure, whether it be a bridge, building, or highway. This refers to the ability to stand strain, wear, and usage; in other words, the fundamental strength that must be inherent in any good building material. The materials themselves must be of sufficient stability to avoid the necessity for frequent repairs and replacements and also to prevent their causing the collapse of structures, accidents that may take a toll of life as well as dollars. Surfacing materials are used for further protection. Paint is applied to prevent the rusting of the steelwork of a bridge, even though the steel itself may have been selected because of its superior wearing qualities.

The toll of damage that is exacted each year because of the corrosion and mechanical wear on structural members runs into millions of dollars. It is a chemical fact that a very minute amount of the steel structure will become dissolved when exposed to the oxygen in water and moist air. A film of hydrogen may form on the iron and quickly retard the further progress of the corrosive effects of the dissolved oxygen. However, if any free oxygen is present, it unites with this hydrogen film, forms water, and allows the process of corrosion to continue. The action can be combated in a variety of ways, and the engineer finds that the wise, safe, and economical course is to provide thoroughly for the protection of outside surfaces against the corrosive effects of air or water. The corrosive process is referred to as "rusting."

Paint is one of the commonest protective substances that the engineer has available to protect the surfaces of his structures. If there has been any corrosive action prior to the application of the paint, the metal must be thoroughly cleaned before applying the coats of paint, or the rusting process will merely continue its destructive work underneath the coats of paint. Asphalts, or coal tars, are also good protective substances. They are used chiefly for roofs or large buildings, such as factories. Layers of a rich concrete, usually two inches thick, have been used with much success when applied to structural steel. If cracks appear in the protective coating, corrosion will commence at these particular spots rather than spread over a wide area. This is called pitting.

In recent years another step has been taken in the protection of surfaces, namely, the plating of various metals. Coatings of nickel, zinc, chromium, and cadmium are effective measures against corrosion.

The mechanical wear of a material is usually caused by abrasion, such as the wearing down of a railroad rail by the continual passing of trains. The failure of a structural part rarely involves structural disaster, because vigilant inspectors will notice it before its condition becomes too serious and will insist upon having it replaced by a new member.

Stone is a material whose characteristics in regard to stability must be watched and determined very accurately. The streakiness that is observed in some older buildings is caused by the action of water working its way through the stone. This is the process that the engineer refers to as weathering. It is just as important as the consideration of strength for building purposes.

When should the engineer use sandstone, and when should he use limestone for a building? Would these materials be better or inferior to such stones as marble and granite? The type of structure that is to be built will answer these questions to a large extent. If stone masonry and brick be applied correctly and with the proper adhesives, the engineer is supplied with a very good structural material. Other questions would be concerned with the effects of water on stone. This may be of no importance in dry countries, but assumes greater importance if the building is to be erected in an area that is subject to a great deal of moisture. Ordinarily, the material that possesses the greatest structural strength is used for large buildings even though its weathering qualities may be inferior to those of another type of stone. It all depends on which characteristic is the more important, and this will be determined by the use to which the stone is to be put. Granite is about the strongest stone that we have from a standpoint of resisting crushing, its ultimate limit ranging from 15,000 to 26,000 pounds per square inch in compression. Marble is next with values of 10,000 to 16,000 pounds per square inch. Limestone and sandstone are next in order, ranging from 3,000 to 20,000 pounds per square inch.

EXPANSION

The expansion of a material is capable of creating serious problems for the engineer. For example, if a railroad construction engineer should be laying rails in the winter time and should lay them with their ends in contact with each other, the heat of the ensuing summer would cause the rails to buckle and destroy the entire system of tracks. Therefore, a little space is left between the rail ends to allow for expansion in summer and contraction in winter. A rail 100 feet long will expand one eighth of an inch with each fifteen-degree rise in temperature. Therefore, from a winter temperature of zero degrees, to a summer temperature of 105 degrees, the 100-foot section of rail will increase seven-eighths of an inch in length. Ordinary sections of rail, however, are thirty feet long, and the expansion and contraction are provided for by leaving a space of approximately one-fourth of an inch between rail ends.

The expansion of the steelwork of a bridge is provided for by making one of the supports into a roller system, so that when the bridge expands or contracts it can move back and forth on the roller and not cause damage by pulling itself loose, as it would do if both supports were fixed and rigid.

If a body that contracts or expands is not allowed to assume new dimensions, it may cause tremendous damage. For instance, those who are familiar with automobiles know the damage that freezing water can do to the engine block. Water will expand upon freezing; when the water of an automobile's cooling system freezes, the excess volume has no place to go, with the result that terrific pressures are set up. If the freezing action is severe enough, the generated pressure may actually be great enough to cause a cracking of the engine block, which is made of cast iron, a strong structural material in itself. Highways have suffered great damage because of the freezing of water that has seeped below their surface. This makes it necessary to devote considerable attention to the design of an effective drainage system for roads. Whole sections of thick concrete have been uplifted to a considerable height by the freezing of water in a roadbed, so great are the powers in play.

VIBRATION

The study of vibration is constantly receiving more and more attention from engineers. The phenomenon can perhaps be best explained by a few illustrations. The swinging back and forth of the pendulum of a clock is one form of vibration. This, however, is an example of vibration that can be seen and measured with no great difficulty. Most materials have such excessive rates of vibration when subjected to the shaking speeds of modern industry that special instruments are necessary for observing the action. These instruments make it possible for the engineer to obtain the data that he must have if he is to make accurate calculations for the design of a structure.

The entire distance of the pendulum's swing is referred to as the "amplitude," and the number of vibrations or swings in a unit time, usually one second, are referred to as the "frequency." Other illustrations of vibrations include those of the strings of a piano or a violin. The violinist, although his instrument has but four strings, can produce many musical notes merely by changing the effective length of the strings. He does this by placing his finger against the string and pressing it against the finger board. If he lengthens the open segment of a string, it will vibrate more slowly and produce a lower note; but, if he shortens the segment, its frequency will increase and a higher note will thus be produced. The action of a piano is similar to this, except for one major difference: for each note there is a string of definite unalterable length. It is set vibrating by the action of a padded hammer that is tripped against the string when the player strikes one of the black or white keys.

A number of men marching over a bridge in step will tend to create hazardous vibration because their steps are successive, regular applications of rhythmic pressure. Since all the footsteps come at the same time they reinforce one another. The continued accumulation of these forces will cause the intensity of the vibrations to increase steadily until such a high degree may be reached that the bridge may be destroyed. Consequently, marching men break step when they cross a bridge; then the vibrations that are set up are created by irregular applications of a multitude of small forces which tend to "dampen," or neutralize, each other.

A railroad train, or any other moving vehicle, on entering a bridge subjects that structure to a force in addition to that created by its own weight. The cause of this additional pressure is the momentum of the train; it produces what is known as "impact force" or "impact load." This fact must be given careful consideration when a bridge is designed. The engineer usually allows for it by doubling the amount of the greatest load that will be on the bridge at any one time. Similar consideration must be taken into account in designing a shop or a building that contains moving machinery.

In the course of investigating the strength of materials, a great deal of time has been devoted to this problem of vibration. It has been studied in many ways; as by bending a small metal beam back and forth rapidly and recording the number of times it bends before it fails. When the angle of bending is small, it may require several million vibrations to break it. On the other hand, if it is bent considerably it may break after only a few thousand vibrations. The same experiment can be performed in another way by placing a small steel rod in a turning lathe and hanging a weight from the middle of the rod. As the rod turns in the lathe, the weight continues to hang downward, so that during each revolution the rod will be bent first one way and then another. This bending will be very slight for a light weight and greater for a heavier weight. The number of turns of the lathe are counted and from this the number of times the rod was bent is determined.

The name of this study is the "reversal of stresses." It is important to the engineer because any structure that is subject to vibration is also subject to a "reversal of stresses." Most structural items, such as beams and girders, that can be bent in one direction can also be bent in the opposite direction.

Sound waves, too, can be damaging to a structure, if their frequency corresponds with the frequency at which the material in the structure will vibrate. There are various interesting examples of this. If a drum is placed near a piano and struck with a drumstick, vibrations will be sent forth that will set into motion the strings of corresponding frequency in the piano so that it will continue to reflect a similar tone. There is a highway bridge in Asheville, North Carolina, that carries an unusual warning sign to the motorist. It cautions him against the sounding of his automobile horn, because the vibrations will make the structure vibrate, and the intensity of some horns may be sufficient to cause the collapse of the bridge. Those who live in cities that have considerable traffic know that a street car or heavy truck can shake a whole house or apartment building. When such a vehicle passes, its pounding on the pavement causes vibrations to pass into the ground and from there to the foundations of nearby buildings, up the columns and across the beams, making it possible for them to be felt by the occupants.

TESTING OF MATERIALS

The American Society for Testing Materials has drawn up many standards of specification and methods of testing building materials. This reasonably assures the engineer of getting the material as it should be; it also gives him a measure of protection to back up his calculations, especially with respect to the loads that are going to be carried by certain structural members. The methods of testing are very detailed and precise work is required to obtain reliable results. This is as it should be, for upon such work depends the general soundness of the material fabric of industry and civilization.

TESTING CEMENT

When collecting a sample of cement for testing, one cannot take out a scoop wherever a convenient place is found. This would not be considered a true sample of the cement according to standard methods. The collector must take his samples from very definite places, not only from the surface of the bin of cement, but at different levels down to the bottom. Portland cement, which is the most common type in use today, is usually tested at the site of its manufacture. A sample of about one pound for every two hundred barrels to be shipped is tested, and this pound must be made up of cement that was evenly distributed among the two hundred barrels. The testing laboratory puts this one pound sample through a series of extremely exhaustive tests to determine conclusively its value for use in structural work. The qualities that are investigated include fineness of grinding, soundness, time required for setting, and tensile strength seven or twenty-eight days after the cement has hardened.

Perhaps one might think that the cross section of a hair is too small to consider when speaking in terms of measurement, but the sieve that tests fineness of grinding is so constructed that a hair will not pass through. It has two hundred holes to the inch, making forty thousand to the square inch. At least ninety-five per cent of the sample of cement must pass through this sieve, each hole of which is just a little less than three one-thousandths of an inch in diameter.

The cement tester must also be adept at a sort of cooking in order that he may perform successfully the test for soundness. A cement "cookie" is made by mixing cement with a prescribed amount of water and working it thoroughly. The mixture is placed on a thin watch-glass with the edges of the "cookie" brought to a very thin point. The glass is placed in a boiler and heated for about five hours. It is then taken out to see whether it still sticks firmly to the glass and shows no cracking on the surface, and whether its edges have peeled, cracked, or turned up.

Another pat of the cement mixture is subjected to tests by small devices called Gilmore needles. They are about the size of a ten-penny nail, with their points flattened and ground to exact dimensions. One needle is equipped with a light weight and the other with a heavy weight. The observer repeatedly rests the lightly weighted needle against the pat until it has set sufficiently to resist any impression being created by the needle point. A careful check on the time is kept. Then the procedure is repeated with the heavier needle until the pat has set sufficiently to resist its force. The two times observed are called the time of initial set and

CHEMIST COL-
LECTING ACCU-
MULATED SAM-
PLES OF FINISHED
CEMENT FOR
TESTING

Courtesy Universal
Atlas Cement Co.

the time of final set; they must fall within limits that have been prescribed or else the cement cannot be classified as acceptable for shipment.

In a previous discussion it was mentioned that concrete possesses tension-resisting qualities, or tensile strength as it is called, only to a limited extent. However, a tensile test is the next that the cement sample must pass. Sand is added to water and cement and a different pat is moulded, one which is called a briquette, an object shaped like a figure eight. The mold is so constructed that the narrow part, or that section corresponding to the middle of the eight, is just exactly one inch thick and one inch wide, providing an area of exactly one square inch. The briquette is placed in water and allowed to harden for seven or twenty-eight days, after which it is placed in a testing machine that has two sets of clamps gripping the piece by its flaring end-sections. A tensile force is applied to the clamps, pulling them in opposite directions until the briquette breaks in two. Again the results must fall within certain limits to prove the fitness of the cement for commercial purposes. The tensile force that seven-day-old briquettes will withstand usually amounts to about two hundred and fifty pounds; since that force is applied over a section one square inch in area, the unit stress is then determined directly as being two hundred and fifty pounds per square inch. For briquettes that have been allowed to stand for twenty-eight days, the stress is usually a little higher, averaging about three hundred and seventy-five pounds per square inch.

SAND

Concrete is not usually thought of as material to be handled with silk gloves; yet the amount of dirt that is present in the sand with which it is made is of great concern. Elaborate steps are taken to guard against the use of sand that is dirty or contains organic matter. Furthermore, each particle of sand must be almost exactly the same size as all the other millions of grains. The engineer, if he is desirous of having his work of the best quality, must devote much time to securing this uniformity. However, this work of measuring sand is not quite as difficult as it may seem. The sizing of the particles is accomplished with a set of six sieves that fit into each other, forming tiers, with the coarsest on the top and the others below successively smaller in mesh. The largest one has four holes to the linear inch, or sixteen to the square inch, allowing all but the coarsest material to pass through. The next sieve below has eight square holes to the linear inch and retains some of the sand that passed through the top layer. The remaining sieves have sixteen, thirty, fifty, and one hundred holes to the linear inch. The last sieve, for example, has ten thousand holes to the square inch. The size of each individual hole is six one-thousandths of an inch and is just about large enough to accommodate two hairs from a person's head. Each sieve retains certain portions of the sand passing through, and the weight of each portion is expressed as a percentage of the original amount. The amount of sand, in order to follow the specifications, must be about equal on all sieves, except that no very great amount should be held by the first or last sieve in the series. This process of measuring the size of the particles is referred to as gradation.

When the sand is tested for its organic matter content, a solution of ordinary household lye is used. A portion of the sand sample is placed in a bottle, and some of the solution poured in with it, enough to cover the surface of the sand. After the mixture has stood for a few days, the color of the liquid above the sand is noted. If it is darker than that of weak tea, there is present in the sand a harmful amount of organic matter, which would seriously lower the structural strength of the concrete.

STONE

The testing that is carried on with stone resembles, to some extent, the work that is done in the testing of sand. Stone is tested for cleanness, size gradation, soundness, and resistance to abrasion. The first two tests are carried out in much the same manner as described for examining sand. The one exception is that the sieve sizes for the gradation test are considerably larger. The holes of the largest sieve are an inch and a half square and those of the smallest are a little less than one-half inch square. The intermediate sizes are usually one inch, three-quarters of an inch, one-half inch, and three-eighths of an inch in diameter.

We do not ordinarily think of water as having much effect upon a block of solid stone. However, water action on material is a very important feature of stone construction that the engineer must investigate fully before using a particular kind of stone for structural work. The test for soundness is one that has been devised to determine in a short time what effects the weather and moisture of the air will have on the building material. The stone is soaked in a saturated solution of sodium sulphate, commonly called Glauber salt. After twenty hours it is dried in an oven for four hours. This twenty-four hour process is repeated from five to twenty times. Any breaking, cracking, or disintegrating in this short period will reveal that the stone cannot withstand the devastating effects of weathering through the years. If any of these defects are apparent to an excessive degree, the stone is rejected for structural use.

The hardness of stone, or its resistance to abrasion and mechanical wear, is determined by the use of a testing device known as the Deval abrasion machine, a cast iron cylinder of approximately eight inches inside diameter and eighteen inches depth. Its cover can be accurately and securely bolted into place. The center line of the cylinder, from top to bottom, makes an angle of thirty degrees with the axle about which the entire drum rotates. A carefully weighed amount of the stone to be tested is placed in the cylinder along with six cast iron balls, each of a diameter of one inch. The machine is rotated at the rate of thirty revolutions per minute, and the test is continued for five hours. At the end of this period the machine is stopped and the contents removed. The broken fragments of stone are carefully collected and weighed, and their weight is expressed as a percentage of the original weight of the sample. This usually amounts to from five to twelve per cent; a stone from which a greater amount than this has been broken is usually considered too soft for structural purposes.

THE FABRIC OF THE FUTURE

Each new material discovered or devised is an additional weapon for the armory of civilization. Any one may change the whole fabric of industry, the aspect of cities, the outward physiognomy of culture. Brick struck the keynote of Sumer and Akkad; stone, that of Egypt. Rome raised her mighty domes and lasting walls with the aid of concrete. Steel might well be called the characteristic material of today, were it not that all materials are receiving attention and being subjected to the processes of research and refinement. Alloys of aluminum and steel are helping the conquest of speed and of the air. Metals and stones, alloys and plastics, woods and cellulose products are multiplying. Inevitably the future will add to the weapons of civilization. Metals as plastic as rubber and plastics as strong as steel are among the possibilities. Rapidly the engineer is being released from bondage to materials of limited use; he can pick and choose, weigh and consider. However, even as various organizations are devoted to testing and standardizing all substances in order that sound construction may proceed from them, so man must test and judge and plan the whole work of engineering and the totality of its structure in order that it may house a harmonious society.

CIVILIZATION has its roots in the soil. From it man gains directly, or indirectly, most of his food and shelter, and all of his clothing; from it he derives also many of those other necessities and luxuries that make up the complexity of his modern life. Agriculture, the science and art of cultivating the soil, long has been and will be his most important interest. The great majority of the world's population obtains its living directly from the soil. Even in teeming cities a large proportion of the people are indirectly dependent upon the soil, earning their living by transporting, processing, or selling farm products. Soil is one of the greatest of all the natural resources which nature has given us. The cultivation of the soil yields man his daily bread; the conservation of the soil assures a nation's future. It is with these two problems—cultivation for a maximum yield today, and conservation for a maximum yield tomorrow—that agricultural engineering is concerned.

SOIL: THE GIFT OF PAST AGES

Soil, like all gifts of Nature, is the product of time. Countless centuries have gone into its making. Sun, wind, and water, grass roots and tree roots, earthworms and bacteria—all have played their part in the development of the soil. Mixed with the finely divided mineral matter, the tiny fragments of rock, are the organic elements of the soil: humus, or decomposed vegetable matter, that retains water and provides much of the plant foods; and minute organisms, some of them too small to be seen under a microscope. It is the variety of their combinations that produces so many different types of soil, each with its own peculiar problems.

Because of their different chemical elements, some soils are excessively acid, or sour, and others extremely alkaline. Some are rich in the minerals essential for plant growth, others deficient.

Texture is another important soil quality, for some soils, due to the size of their particles, are very coarse, while others are exceedingly fine. Soils also vary widely in structure; in some the particles are so arranged that good circulation of air and water is possible; others are virtually water-logged.

On the basis of these and other qualities the soils of the world are commonly divided into several major groups, each of which includes many varieties. Broadly speaking, however, the qualities of soils in any one group are the same, and the problems of their utilization and conservation are similar.

THE SOILS OF THE FORESTS

In the hot, humid lands of low latitude, the laterites, or red earths, are developed, under a forest cover. These soils, because of the speed with which rock decays in such regions, form very rapidly and are often very deep. However, because of heavy rainfall and rapid bacterial action, they are just as quickly deprived of their plant foods and are soon eroded and washed away. For this reason it is common in the tropical rain forests of Africa and South America for the natives to migrate from one plot of land to another. A clearing is made in the forest, the plant is sown and harvested for a year or two, and then the tribe moves on to repeat the process.

Other red soils, similar to the laterites, are found throughout the Southern states. In this region a farmer commonly clears and cultivates a patch of land for a few seasons, and then moves on to another. It is on these red, subtropical soils that much of our cotton is grown. Long-continued planting of the land with this crop has exhausted the soil in many regions. In fact, throughout the entire South, erosion has resulted in excessive loss of topsoil, sometimes even in the complete destruction of the soil. It is with the problems of this soil type that the Tennessee Valley Authority is in large part concerned.

These red, subtropical soils vary widely as to fertility. Some, such as the coffee-producing soils of Brazil, yield year after year, while others are rapidly exhausted. Some, particularly the true laterites, are so sterile that they contain little more than oxides of iron or aluminum, and are mined as mineral ores. In their most

Courtesy Soil Conservation Service, U. S. Dept. of Agriculture

WHAT EROSION DID TO ONE OKLAHOMA FARM

fertile period these soils supported fine forests, which could be made to yield better returns than any other type of crop on such lands.

A distinctly different type of soil is the podsol, or gray earth, of the cold, humid lands of the world. This soil, developed under a coniferous forest, forms very slowly, is very shallow, and, due to the slowness of decay in such regions, is highly acid. Extremely infertile, this soil's chief use is in the production of the evergreen forest. For that purpose it is employed in northern Russia and Canada.

In the United States podsols occur in the region of the upper Great Lakes and northern New England. Their cultivation has given rise to many problems of rural resettlement. The soil, though it often contains enough plant food to produce a good yield or two, is exhausted rapidly, and leaves the farmer stranded on his land. Such soils once produced magnificent stands of white pine, and they can again be made to do so.

In eastern United States and in the region of the Ohio Valley is an intermediate soil type, the gray-brown podsolic soils. These were originally fertile, but, because they have been long cultivated, much of their fertility has been lost. Useful production is obtained from them by well-managed agricultural engineering practices: crop rotation, conservative types of plowing and cultivating, and widespread use of animal and chemical fertilizers. These podsolic soils, which are developed under a broadleaf forest in a temperate climate, are also the prevailing type in northern and western Europe and northern China, regions of similar vegetation and climate. In Europe, conservation of this type of soil has long been practiced. In northern China, on the other hand, centuries of cultivation have so depleted the soil that vast areas of once fertile lands are now barren.

THE PRAIRIE SOILS

In contrast to the previously described soils, each developed under a forest cover in regions of heavy or ample rainfall, are the soils of the dry lands, regions of grass or desert, having moderate or very little rainfall.

Upon the grassland soils of the world—those soils which, because of their high humus content, are characteristically dark brown to black—have developed the great "bread baskets" of the nations. In America these are the prairies and plains of the Mississippi Valley, the vast wheat and corn lands of the continent. On similar soils are the great wheat fields of the Argentine Pampas, the rich cereal lands of Australia, and the vast grain belt of southern Russia.

The cultivation of these dark, rich soils, developed under the thick prairie sod, is relatively new to mankind. Their development awaited the coming of the steel plow; more primitive instruments could not break the tough crust. They are, in consequence, relatively fresh and highly productive, and they are amply able to supply all the needs of cultivated plants. Besides, since they are commonly on flat or gently rolling land, they are not so subject to erosion as are the older, podsolic soils. However, even within the century they have been cultivated, they have been stripped of much of their original fertility. Today, the problem of maintaining their productivity and of preventing their being washed or blown away is one of the chief concerns of the conservation engineer. These soils represent the greatest national wealth; they are a natural heritage that must be carefully guarded against erosion and depletion.

In America, west of the belt of grassland soils, are the brown soils of the high plains. These, developed in regions of rainfall insufficient to support a dense growth of grasses, are the semi-arid soils of the region now known as the "dust bowl." They are fertile but they are loosely held together. Over-grazing in earlier years and more particularly recent over-cultivation have stripped them of their cover and exposed them to the ravages of the wind, so that the land of whole counties has been literally blown off the map.

Improved agricultural prac-tices will lessen the damages of erosion, but throughout large areas the only solution to this

Courtesy Soil Conservation Service, U. S. Dept. of Agriculture

SHEET EROSION AND GULLYING CAUSED BY CONTINUOUS UP-AND-DOWN CULTIVATION

problem is to restore the natural vegetation, the grasses and shrubs which formerly held the soil together. Steps are being taken to accomplish this restoration by returning many acres to a fallow state, a rest cure, so to speak; by the planting of trees to form a shelter belt, thereby increasing the vegetation and reducing the damage of the wind; and by the carefully managed farming or grazing of the less-damaged areas. The land cannot be plowed indefinitely, for it then blows away; so its ultimate use will prob-ably be for grazing. Similar soils, with similar problems, lie on the desert boundaries of grasslands throughout the world.

THE ENGINEER RESTORES THE DESERT

The drab, gray soils of the desert have long been cultivated under irrigation. The use of water on such soils is twofold in purpose: it is essential for plant growth, and it is needed to carry away the excess alkalis that give the soil its characteristically light color.

The problem of irrigation is one of the oldest in the history of agriculture. Though always expensive, it has sometimes been extraordinarily successful. Desert soils are often very fertile, for the low rainfall of arid regions results in little loss of plant food through erosion or leaching. Furthermore, such soils lie in lands of abundant sunshine, a factor of utmost importance in the cultivation of all green plants.

It is for these reasons, in addition to that of supplying arable land to the peoples of arid regions, that irrigation projects are still being developed at a time when vast acreages of humid lands are being withdrawn from agricultural production. The former are new and rich, and if carefully managed they can be made to yield indefinitely. The latter are old and worn out; they need a rest.

Water has always been of fundamental importance to man. The fear of flood and the fear of drought are elemental to him, for it seems there is always too much or too little water. This is not true, of course, but it is true that the chief problem of agricultural engineering is that of controlling the amount and distribution of water in and on the soil. Water in the soil is essential to plant growth. Cultivated plants require from one hundred to one thousand times as much water per year as the weight of their dry tissues. Furthermore, plants are dependent upon water for their nourishment, for the plant foods are obtained only in solution. Quantities of nitrogen, potassium, phosphorus, and other plant nutrients may be present in the soil, but if they are not in the proper chemical relationship, and if they are not in solution, they are of no use to the plant. On the other hand too much water in the soil is injurious to most forms of agricultural production. The problem of maintaining the proper amount of water in the soil is therefore paramount. This problem may be solved by such engineering projects as irrigating dry lands, draining wet lands, and plowing and cultivating in such a way as to obtain and maintain the proper amount of water in the soil.

THE ENGINEER PREVENTS EROSION

But the present-day concern is with the problem of the destructive action of running water on cultivated land. Nature, which builds up the soil slowly, if left to herself, removes it slowly. She protects the soil with a mantle of vegetation, which holds the rain waters, allowing them to drain slowly away. The disastrous floods that ruin the labor of modern man were less frequent in the time of his primitive forefathers. Before the soil was cultivated it did not wash away so extensively, and rivers carried off the annual heavy rains and melting snows more gradually.

The problem, then, is to cultivate the land in such a way that water falling upon it is not allowed to run off rapidly, carrying with it the wealth of the soil and causing disastrous floods on the rivers. This must be done or the soil will be washed away down to the sea and lost forever.

The National Resources Board reported that the annual losses of plant foods from the crop lands and pastures of this country through leaching and erosion are about six times greater than the quantity of those elements removed by the plants themselves. Already the utility of about thirty-five million acres of formerly good farm land has been destroyed. From about one hundred and twenty-five million additional acres the topsoil has been largely removed by erosion. And at least one hundred million acres of cultivated land are well on their way to the same fate.

Retiring the land from agriculture would stop this appalling waste of the nation's wealth, and this may be done with the steeper slopes and the worn-out soils. But the good farm lands must be tilled. To work these lands with a minimum of soil loss several forms of cultivation have been developed. Most effective of all is terracing, a method of erosion control used for centuries in older countries, and now increasingly employed throughout the United States. In the South, terracing is already common. It not only prevents gullying, but stops sheet erosion, a washing away of the topsoil that, although imperceptible in operation, goes on at an alarming rate. It is estimated that the state of Iowa, level as it is, has lost several inches of her topsoil largely by sheet erosion, during the short period her lands have been cultivated.

It has been found in the Tennessee Valley that terraces laid at intervals across the fields retain from eighty-five to ninety per cent of the rainfall. This means that water seeps gently through the soil, is available to the plants, and is finally emptied into the streams and rivers as clear ground water. This in turn prevents floods and reduces the accumulation of silt in dams, which are sometimes filled with silt in as short a time as five years.

PROTECTING THE SOIL

Simplest of all soil-protection methods is contour plowing, a practice that is being used increasingly in America. By this means the little gullies formed by the plow are made to run across the slope of the land, rather than with it. As a result, water falling on the land is stopped by each furrow instead of being encouraged to race down the slope. Enormous saving of topsoil is effected in this manner, and the water is conserved for plant use. Equally important as a conservation measure is the protection afforded the soil by a winter crop. This is particularly true in the South, where no snow cover is provided by nature, and where the ground is rarely frozen to any appreciable degree.

For land that is already badly eroded two other forms of protection are effective. One is the construction of little dams across the gullies, thereby filling them in and preventing further washing away. The other is to convert the land to pasture, or to plant it with such deeply rooted plants as those of the clover family. Alfalfa, for example, not only greatly enriches the soil, but very materially lessens erosion. It has been found that land of moderate slope, planted in alfalfa, loses only some five per cent of the rainfall, whereas open, fallow soil loses six times as much. Similarly, it has been demonstrated that from an acre of fallow soil more than one hundred tons of soil are sometimes washed away in a year's time, whereas from a comparable acre sown with alfalfa only a fraction of a ton is lost. And on an acre upon which practical rotation of corn, wheat, and clover is practiced the average annual loss is only thirteen tons. It is evident, therefore, that the nature of the crop is in itself a prime factor in controlling soil erosion.

Courtesy Soil Conservation Service, U. S. Dept. of Agriculture

CONTOUR CULTIVATION AND STRIP CROPPING CONTROL EROSION

THE ENGINEER AND THE DUST BOWL

Another type of erosion, that accomplished by the wind, presents a different problem. In the eastern and southeastern United States farming practices must be adjusted to heavy rainfall. In the West, however, the factor of prime concern is not the damage done by running water, but the havoc wrought by the wind. In the "dust bowl" region, where the normal rainfall is rarely more than sufficient, every drop that falls must be conserved, both to nourish the plants and to anchor the topsoil. Several methods of cultivation have been developed to retain the maximum amount of moisture in the soil.

Most effective is the process of "listing." This method of tilling the land is preferable to the more common one of disk tilling, because the lister forms small ditches, or basins, which catch and retain the rainfall, allowing it to seep into the soil, where it is stored. Other methods tend to pulverize the soil to such a degree that it becomes impervious to water. Furthermore, the lister does not break up the soil as does the disk type of plow. Clods on the surface tend to protect the finer particles below and prevent them from blowing away.

Contour listing is highly effective, especially if the ditches are dammed at intervals, a feat performed automatically by a simple attachment to the machine. An experiment with two Kansas fields, one listed with dams every ten feet, the soil of the other finely pulverized, indicated the efficiency of this type of cultivating. A two-and-a-half inch rain fell for thirty minutes. The listed field held the water with no runoff; on the other field two-thirds of the water was lost, carrying with it soil at the rate of seventeen tons per acre. Good agricultural engineering methods can go a long way toward solving the problems of the "dust bowl."

Cultivated land suffers not only the depredations of wind and water. Under bad farming methods it quickly loses its fertility. Continued cultivation, particularly if it be limited to one crop, soon exhausts the soil. To offset this drain on the soil, crop rotation is widely practiced. Corn and wheat, for example, are often varied with a legume, such as soy beans or alfalfa. The latter is particularly valuable, for its root serves as a host to bacteria that carry the nitrogen from the air into the soil.

The centuries-old practice of letting the land lie fallow, giving it a rest for a year or two, allows nature to replenish the plant food, both from the rock below and the decaying vegetation above. Application of manufactured fertilizers, in addition to the use of barnyard manure, is a conservation practice that amply pays for itself. Liming the soil with simple crushed limestone corrects acidity and improves large areas of farm land. Of the artificial fertilizers, those manufactured of packing-house waste are most common. These are generally made with a high content of potash.

The phosphates and nitrates, however, are more expensive. With the purpose of effecting an economical manufacturing

DESTRUCTION

Courtesy Soil Conservation Service, U. S. Dept. of Agriculture

PROTECTION

process, the Tennessee Valley Authority is experimenting with phosphates and nitrates at Wilson Dam, using the old plant built for nitrate production during the World War. The economical production of these valuable forms of plant food would mean much to American agriculture.

Synthetic plant foods have been the subject of experiment for many years, but they are still in the laboratory stage. It is quite possible to grow almost any of the cultivated plants in air, water, and sunshine, with the aid of these highly concentrated nutrients. But as yet the expense of their production does not permit their practical application. It seems certain that man for some time to come will continue to till the soil. And in the future development of the farm lies another phase of agricultural engineering—the improvement of farm implements and the mechanization of agriculture.

AGRICULTURAL IMPLEMENTS

Along with the flint knives and arrowheads of early man, archaeologists often find crude farming implements which testify that agriculture was second only to hunting among the occupations of early man. When, some thousands of years ago, a savage bound his war-ax to a forked stick and used it to till the soil, a rudimentary plow was created. The prophecy in the Bible that "they shall beat their swords into plowshares" indicated that plows of wood and stone had been replaced by sturdier tools of iron. Throughout the Middle Ages progress in agricultural devices remained almost stationary. Cumbersome plows of wood, sometimes covered with scraps of metal, were the instruments commonly used by the serfs of great feudal estates. Often these awkward affairs were drawn by harnessed peasants.

The Pilgrims brought the farming methods of England to the New World, but found them unsuited to working the boulder-strewn fields of Massachusetts. Instructed by Squanto and other friendly Indians, they soon developed a method of agriculture that combined Indian and European techniques.

The opening of the Mississippi Valley afforded a great impetus to the development of the plow and to all of American agriculture. The vast tracts of prairie soil, rich with the packed humus of centuries, defied cultivation by European methods. In Ohio, Illinois, Kansas, Iowa, and other states, there were thousands of fertile acres whose surface was barely scratched by the laborious farming procedure of the early nineteenth century. Shovel plows, bull plows, and bar-share plows were in common use.

Cast-iron plows made their appearance in 1819, with improved methods of smelting, and these implements enabled the pioneers to furrow the tough prairie sod. To the plow as much as to the railroad belongs the credit for the rapid settling of the West.

Second only to the plow, the sickle has been a principal weapon in man's conquest of nature since the beginning of recorded history. Like the plow, the sickle also had its origin in war-like pursuits. Copeland, noting primitive agrarian methods, observes that "at the period of the Roman Conquest the scythe was not only employed in agriculture by the Britons, but also as a weapon of warfare, being attached to the axles of their chariots." This simple instrument, which did duty in war or peace, was known to the Romans, but its use was not common in Europe until after the fourteenth century. In the early years of the Industrial Revolution many inventors made experiments with new forms of scythes, but their efforts for the most part were unsuccessful.

MECHANIZED AGRICULTURE

The first mechanical reaper of practical importance was that invented by Cyrus Hall McCormick, who successfully demonstrated his machine in a field near Steele's Tavern, Virginia, in July, 1831. Here as last was a device with which the long stretches of the prairie could be harvested with a minimum of man power. McCormick patented his reaper in 1834. This feeble forerunner of today's great harvesters sold for one hundred dollars.

The McCormick reaper signalized the beginning of agricultural mechanization. Cast iron was being used to manufacture farm implements, and crude cultivators were coming into use throughout the eastern states. In 1836, Moore invented an ancestor of the modern combine, a bulky machine pulled by sixteen horses; this machine, nonetheless, cut, threshed, cleaned, and sacked wheat more rapidly than hand labor. One of Moore's combines was taken by ship around Cape Horn to California, where it operated in the San José Valley until 1854. At its best, Moore's machine was able to sack twenty acres a day.

By the middle of the nineteenth century engineers of the United States had begun to surpass those of Europe in the development of agricultural apparatus. An improved reaper was placed on the market, and in 1856 the Bessemer steel process was perfected. Plows, harrows, and other farm implements manufactured of steel quickened the pace of American agriculture.

Educators, meanwhile, were beginning to realize that agriculture was a science upon which, to a great extent, depended the future of the nation. Yale University had recognized this fact long before, and had created a chair in agricultural chemistry for John Pitkin Norton in 1847. Professor Norton's book, *Elements of Scientific Agriculture,* had a large circulation during the latter half of the nineteenth century.

In 1850 Jonathan Baldwin Turner, of Jacksonville, Illinois, became interested in the educational aspects of agriculture and proceeded to do pioneer work in the field. As a result of Turner's activities, Senator Justin S. Morrill of Vermont introduced a bill in 1857 to establish agricultural colleges. The bill was passed five years later and was signed by President Lincoln. It provided for the sale of public lands in each of the states, proceeds of which were to be devoted to the "endowment, support, and maintenance of colleges to teach such branches of learning as are related to agriculture and the mechanic arts."

The Morrill Act has resulted in the creation of the so-called land-grant colleges in each of the forty-eight states as well as in the territories of Alaska, Porto Rico, and Hawaii. Today there are sixty-nine land-grant colleges, including seventeen agricultural and mechanical schools for Negroes in the Southern states. The agricultural college is connected with the state university in about half the states and territories; in the remainder it is generally combined with the state engineering division. Only one school created by the Morrill Act, Massachusetts Agricultural College at Amherst, is devoted solely to agriculture. The others offer the

Courtesy International Harvester Company

CONTOUR CROPPING WITH A SPRING-TOOTH HARROW

Courtesy International Harvester Company

A TRACTOR-POWERED CORN SHELLER AT WORK
The output of this equipment is from 150 to 250 bushels per hour.

usual college curricula, in addition to agricultural studies. The Congress which passed the Morrill Act also passed the Homestead Act, and created the Department of Agriculture. Aided by the land-grant colleges, agricultural engineering advanced rapidly in the decades following the Civil War. The foundation of the agricultural sciences, which today include botany, chemistry, physics, physiology, nutrition, soil sciences, genetics, pathology, parasitology, bacteriology, and entomology, was laboriously laid by professors who, in this instance, could not benefit from the stored-up knowledge of mankind. Gradually, through countless experiments, applied agricultural science came to include agronomy, floriculture, forestry, horticulture, olericulture, animal husbandry, apiculture, dairy culture, pisciculture, and sericulture.

The Hatch Act of 1887 and the Adams Act of 1906 further encouraged agricultural engineering by establishing fifty-six experimental farms for testing soils and crops and for improving animal husbandry. Most of the experimental stations are under the supervision of land-grant colleges.

AGRICULTURAL ENGINEERING

With the extension and development of agricultural research have come the invention and improvement of countless farm implements and machines, the development of superior crops and farm animals, the rise of strictly specialized agriculture, and an increasingly high standard of life on the farm. The perfection of the gasoline engine, the evolution of the tractor, the development of self-contained power plants, and the extension of rural electrification have brought farm engineering closer to the ultimate in efficiency. Of the hundreds of farm implements on the market today, nearly fifty are in common use on American farms. For harvesting there are binders, headers, harvester-threshers, windrow harvesters, and reapers. For haying there are mowers, rakes, tedders, loaders, and stackers. And for corn cultivation there are planters, listers, drills, cultivators, binders, ensilage cutters, ensilage harvesters, ensilage blowers, and corn pickers, shellers, huskers, and shredders.

A score of tillage implements are available to the farmer whose forefathers some hundred years ago had to rely on hoe, rake, and plow. Specialized tools for the cultivation of beets, cotton, rice, and fruit have been perfected. Weeders, rotary hoes, feed grinders, potato diggers, land packers, and lime spreaders are but a few of the many devices that have appeared in answer to diverse needs.

Indicative of the trend of American agriculture are the rice fields of Texas and Louisiana, where the staple food of the Orient is produced entirely by machine methods. American rice, produced more economically than that of the East, is actually exported to Japan. Perhaps more striking is the use of the airplane in modern agriculture. Cotton fields attacked by boll-weevils are speedily defended by low-flying planes that dust the plants with an insecticide. In the fruit industry the smudge pot has taken to the air, for airplanes lay down the blanket of smoke that protects valuable crops from destruction by frost.

But perhaps more revolutionary still, in its implications, is the recent development of the cotton picker. From earliest days the cultivation of cotton has been wholly manual, but recent tests have proved the practicability of the mechanical cotton picker. Without a doubt, cotton, last of the important crops requiring manual attention, will be picked by machine, as the device is improved.

IT IS TRUE that engineering has done a great work in applying the achievements of science to the creation of an impressive materialistic civilization. It is a painstaking and unheralded function and is performed by men and women in many occupations. A useful tool, it is always a part of other work. Yet few activities in modern society have been so glowingly publicized as has engineering. Flamboyant praises and bitter execrations have streamed above the heads of its obscure workers while they patiently went about their designing and testing, amazed at the hubbub. They were startled at attempts to cloak one part of their work in glamour, and they laughed at the weird proposals of "technocracy."

They knew nothing of the heroics that were attached to their work, and in many cases the term "engineer" was thrust upon them in an entirely meaningless fashion. Sailors and psychologists as well as bookkeepers and chemists learned with surprise that they were engineers and that they were remaking the world. They knew that their materials were the work of scientists and that their methods were the borrowed techniques of science. Until the title "engineers" was tacked on, most of them thought of themselves simply as machine designers, architects, surveyors, electricians, or auditors. They were the hirelings of industry, and their imagination and ingenuity in the application of scientific discoveries were often subjected to dictation by profit-seeking industry rather than by the real needs of mankind.

There are some classifications of engineers whose functions are definite, but in many instances engineering is merely a linking activity performed in part by academic research scientists and in part by factory workers and operators of machines. In this broad sense engineering is not new and it is not specialized. Considered as the application of abstract science to the material problems of living, engineering is practiced everywhere and every man or woman is an engineer.